QUESTIONS & ANSWERS

Electric Motors

A. J. Coker
revised by
Philip Chapman

Newnes Technical Books

Published by Newnes Technical Books
an imprint of Newnes Books,
a division of The Hamlyn Publishing Group Limited,
84–88 The Centre, Feltham, Middlesex, TW13 4BH,
and distributed for them by
The Hamlyn Publishing Group Limited
Rushden, Northants, England.

First published 1965
Second edition 1976
    Reprinted 1977, 1978, 1979, 1982, 1985 with revisions

ISBN 0 408 00200 X

Printed in England by Whitstable Litho Limited

CONTENTS

PREFACE

This book has been written for students, apprentices and technicians who need a basic introduction to electric motors. This edition maintains the philosophy of the previous one by providing information on the practical aspects of a.c. and d.c. motors and their associated control gear for all those concerned with the use, installation, operation and maintenance of motors in industry and elsewhere.

Several developments have taken place in the technology of electric motors since the appearance of the first edition of this book, and probably the most marked advance has been in the application of solid-state devices to the control of motors. The linear motor also has experienced a somewhat spectacular rise to prominence, mainly due to its potential for propulsion of mass transport systems. These two topics are dealt with in some detail. Other new features include the more recently developed types of motor-pole amplitude modulated motors, reluctance motors – and new standards relating to motor ratings.

This edition has been completely metricated and thus encourages the reader to think in metric terms rather than to go through the tedious process of conversion wherever motor power ratings, torques, etc. are quoted. S.I. units are used throughout.

It is hoped that this new edition will be as well received as its forerunner by all those students, apprentices and technicians who need a basic grounding in the practical aspects of electric motors.

P.C.

1

INTRODUCTION

What is the standard a.c. supply voltage in Great Britain ?
Fifty-hertz, 240/415 volts, indicating 3-phase supply at 415 volts for 3-phase loads connected to the three phase lines, 3-phase 4-wire supply for connecting 240-volt single-phase loads between one or other of the phase lines and neutral, and single-phase 415-volt supply for single-phase loads connected between two phase lines.

What is phase voltage ?
The voltage between any phase wire of a 3-phase supply and the neutral wire.

What is the relationship between the phase voltage and the line voltage of a 3-phase 4-wire system ?
Line voltage $= 1 \cdot 732 \times$ phase voltage.

What is a 3-wire d.c. supply system ?
A system consisting of positive and negative outers and a middle or neutral wire. The voltage between the outers is twice the voltage between either outer and neutral. For example, a 220/440-volt d.c. supply is one having 440 volts between outers and 220 volts between each outer and neutral.

What is meant by the torque of a motor ?
The turning effort developed by the motor, usually

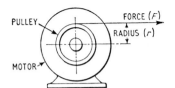

Fig. 1.—*The torque of a motor*

Torque is force (F) multiplied by the radius of action (r). If F is in newtons and r is in metres the torque will be given in newton metres (Nm).

expressed in so many newton metres (Nm). If the motor exerts a force of F N acting at right angles to a radius of r m from the centre of its pulley, the resulting torque is $F \times r$ Nm.

How is the torque of a motor produced?

The production of torque requires the interaction of two sets of magnetic fields. The usual arrangement is for these fields to be produced by two sets of windings, both carrying current derived from the supply. One set of windings is situated on the stationary outer member (stator or field poles) and the other set on the rotating member (rotor or armature).

The principle is illustrated in the accompanying diagram. This shows a coil free to rotate about its axis in a magnetic field. If the coil is supplied with current, or a current is induced to flow in it, as indicated, the magnetic flux associated with this current will interact with the magnetic-field flux and produce a force on each side of the coil, creating a torque about the axis and causing rotation of the coil as indicated.

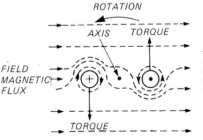

Fig. 2.—*How the torque of a motor is produced*

The magnetic-field flux interacts with the magnetic flux due to the current flowing in the conductors of the coil.

8

The principle is the same whether the currents producing the two fields originate from a.c. or d.c. supplies.

In the d.c. motor, the magnetic-field system is fixed and the current fed to the rotating armature coils is changed in direction in the coils by means of brushes and commutator.

CONVENTIONAL SIGNS
⊙ CURRENT FLOWING TOWARDS OBSERVER
⊕ CURRENT FLOWING AWAY FROM OBSERVER

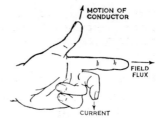

Fig. 3.—Conventional signs for magnetic polarity, direction of current and direction of rotation.

The magnetic lines of force are assumed to leave the face of a north pole.

Fig. 4.—The direction of rotation of a motor is obtained by the use of Fleming's left-hand rule.

Direction of rotation depends on the direction of the main-field flux and the direction of the currents in the rotor or armature conductors.

In a.c. motors of the induction type, the stator windings are usually distributed in slots around the stator core. These windings are connected to the supply and the rotating field produced by them induces currents to flow in the rotor windings.

What torques must be considered when driving a machine ?

(1) The initial starting (breakaway) torque needed to overcome the static friction and inertia of the driven machine and thus start it away from standstill.

(2) The accelerating torque needed to run the driven machine up to full speed.

(3) The running torque when full speed is reached.

How can the initial starting torque needed for a driven machine be found ?

One method is to wrap a cord attached to a spring

balance around the half-coupling or pulley of the driven machine and to give a steady pull, noting the force required to start the shaft rotating.

The starting torque required by the driven machine in newton metres is equal to

Pull (N) × radius of half-coupling or pulley (m)

An alternative method is to fix a bar along the horizontal diameter of the pulley and hang weights on the bar at a known distance from the centre of the pulley until the pulley begins to turn.

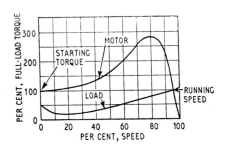

Fig. 5.—Torque/speed curves of a motor and its load

The motor curve is for a squirrel-cage induction motor. The area between the two curves indicates the torque available to accelerate the load.

How is the accelerating torque determined ?

From the torque/speed curves of the motor and the load. The point at which the torque/speed curves intersect will be where the final running speed occurs. The motor torque available for accelerating the driven machine at a particular speed corresponds to the difference between motor torque and load torque at that speed.

What is meant by the power of a motor ?

Its mechanical output or rate of doing work—the work it does per unit of time (per minute or per second). The power rating of a motor is measured in watts, or more usually, kilowatts. Motor power was formerly measured in horse-power. 1 h.p. = 746 watts.

How is the torque of a motor related to its power?

The motor exerts a force F acting at right-angles to the radius r of its shaft or pulley. Its torque is force multiplied by radius (torque = $F \times r$).

The work the motor does *in one revolution* of the motor pulley is equal to the force exerted (F) multiplied by the circumference of the pulley ($2\pi r$), that is, $F \times 2\pi r$.

The work done by the motor *in one minute* is its mechanical output or power and this is equal to work done per revolution $\times$ r.p.m., that is,

$$F \times 2\pi r \times \text{r.p.m.}$$

As we have already seen, $F \times r$ is the torque, so work done per minute =

mechanical output = $2\pi \times$ r.p.m. $\times$ torque

If torque is in Nm, the power in watts is obtained by dividing by 60, which gives (1 Watt = 1 Nm/sec)

$$\text{Power of motor} = \frac{2\pi \times \text{torque (Nm)} \times \text{r.p.m.}}{60}$$

Motors can be divided into two main classes in respect of their characteristic performance. What are these?

Shunt characteristic and series characteristic.

What is a shunt characteristic?

The characteristic of motors that have a fairly constant speed independent of load conditions within their working range from no-load to full-load. This type of characteristic is required for most industrial and many other applications and is largely met by the use of three-phase and single-phase induction motors.

What is a series characteristic?

The characteristic of motors that have a high torque at

starting and at low speed, as well as a tendency for speed to rise on light load. Such motors would not be used when a steady speed is necessary unless the load is constant. They are well suited to traction and crane applications. In fractional-kilowatt sizes, the universal motor, which has a series characteristic, is widely used.

What is meant by the time rating of a motor?

Some motors are required to carry full load all day, others to run only for a series of short periods on full load, say a few minutes at a time. The less time a motor is actually in operation over a period, the more time it has to cool down between spells of operation and the smaller its frame size needs to be. It is economical in practice therefore to classify motors as to their time rating. Various time ratings have become standardised: maximum continuous rating, short time rating or some special rating based on a particular duty cycle. The manufacturer guarantees that the motor will not exceed a certain temperature after being run on full load for a certain length of time. These are often referred to as "continuous" or "intermittent" ratings.

What is maximum continuous rating?

This is a statement of the load and conditions assigned to the machine by the manufacturer at which the machine may be operated for an unlimited period.

What is short time rating?

This is again a statement of the load and conditions under which the machine may be operated but this time for a limited period only, starting at ambient temperature. There are several preferred periods for which short time rating may apply, these being 10, 30, 60 and 90 minutes.

For what type of application does a short time rating apply?

Applications with fairly intermittent periods of operation, such as cranes, hoists, lifts and certain machine tools that are operated only infrequently.

What is meant by the temperature rating of a motor?

The rated output of a motor is controlled by the temperature that the winding insulation is capable of withstanding. The maximum-permissible-operating temperature depends on the type of insulation and the classifications in more general use are:

Class A—cotton, silk, paper and similar organic materials when suitably impregnated.

Class E—materials or combinations of materials that are capable of operating at a higher temperature than Class A.

Class B—Mica, asbestos, glass fibre, and similar inorganic binding substances.

Class H—mica paper composites, e.g. three layers of glass cloth, mica paper and polyester film bonded with varnish to provide tough, flexible insulation.

How is the power required to drive an individual machine decided?

The power required is best obtained from the maker of the machine to be driven. In many applications the power required depends upon the efficiency of the driven machine and this can only be estimated by its manufacturer. This particularly applies to pumps, compressors, generators, centrifugal separators and fans.

For driving machine tools, the required power is increased for heavy duty and rapid production and reduced when only light work is the rule.

What calculation is commonly used to determine the minimum power required when the loads to be driven vary over a particular work cycle?

The minimum power required to avoid overheating is determined approximately by the root-mean-square method:

$$\text{Power} = \sqrt{\frac{(P_1)^2\, t_1 + (P_2)^2\, t_2 + (P_3)^2\, t_3 + \ldots}{\text{Total time of one cycle of operation}}}$$

where P_1, P_2, P_3, etc are the powers required during the duty cycle and t_1, t_2, t_3, etc. are the periods of time in minutes corresponding to the above power demands.

How is power decided for driving a lineshaft belted to a group of machines?

If there is a sufficient number of machines, say six or more, and these are hand-controlled so that there are pauses during which no work is being done, such as for setting up, the motor power will seldom exceed half the sum of the requirements of the driven machines. A more powerful motor will be necessary when the driven machines are on full-capacity work all the time.

What is the power required for driving cranes, hoists and winches?

$$\text{Power} = \frac{\text{weight lifted in kg} \times \text{lifting speed in m/s}}{9.81 \times \text{efficiency of mechanical parts}}$$

An efficiency of about 0·70 may be assumed for worm and spur gearing or 0·65 if a stage of friction gearing is incorporated as in a friction hoist. These are average figures that may be exceeded in certain favourable cases. On the other hand, they may easily be less, requiring more power if the gear train consists of many stages or if badly cut or worn or if cast gears are employed.

How is the current required to supply a 3-phase motor at full-load calculated?

From details of power, efficiency and power factor. The current is equal to

$$\frac{\text{Power} \times 100}{1·732 \times \text{line voltage} \times \% \text{ efficiency} \times \text{power factor}}$$

14

How is the full-load current of a single-phase motor arrived at?

From the formula

$$\frac{\text{Power} \times 100}{\text{Voltage} \times \% \text{ efficiency} \times \text{power factor}} = \text{current}$$

How is the full-load current of a d.c. motor calculated?

From the formula

$$\frac{\text{Power} \times 100}{\text{Voltage} \times \% \text{ efficiency}} = \text{current}$$

What is power factor ?

The factor or percentage of the current in an a.c. circuit that is supplied in the form of energy, the remaining current being idle. This idle current is termed reactive current or wattless current.

The power factor of a circuit is calculated from $\frac{\text{kW}}{\text{kVA}}$

If an induction motor is described as having a power factor of 80 per cent or 0·8, what does this mean ?

That 80 per cent of the motor current at full load is power current, doing work, and 20 per cent is idle. A kVA demand meter or an ammeter will register the full 100 per cent of current but a wattmeter will take into account only the true energy component of the current, namely 80 per cent.

An additional point about an induction motor is that the idle or wattless current is lagging.

How does lagging wattless current arise ?

Every induction motor (or transformer or other electrical apparatus comprising coils of wire embedded in or surrounding an iron core) constitutes an inductive reactance.

15

If the motor is switched on to an a.c. supply, whether it does useful work or not, a current is taken from the system to excite it. This current is 90° lagging in phase on the voltage and is reactive current or so-called idle or wattless current. The only energy in this current is that required to overcome the losses and is but a small fraction of the total.

When the motor is put to work, it will take, in addition to its excitation current, a power or energy current according to the amount of work to be done and the efficiency loss in the motor. The proportion of the two currents varies according to the percentage load on the motor. Consequently, the nearer the motor runs to full power the greater will be the proportion of power current to idle current, i.e. the higher the power factor.

What is meant by power-factor correction ?

Excitation current is an essential feature of a.c. induction motors (and other a.c. inductive apparatus). The demand for excitation current exists whether the motor runs loaded or light. If this current circulates back and forth in the supply system, the supply cables, alternators and other equipment have to be designed to carry it and the additional expense involved is passed on to the consumer in higher price per kWh. A low power factor on the supply involves the locking up of capital by the supply authority in order to carry heavy idle current. However, the user can arrange to reduce the excitation currents carried by the supply by improving the power factor of his installation. To enable supply authorities to turn idle capital into revenue-producing capital, they offer a tariff that in effect gives a substantial bonus to those consumers who improve the power factor of their load.

How can power factor be improved ?

By the installation of static capacitors, by the provision

of d.c. exciters as used in synchronous motors, or by the use of compensated motors or rotary phase-advancers. These provide the necessary excitation current for the motors and thus relieve the supply system of a portion or the whole of the wattless lagging current.

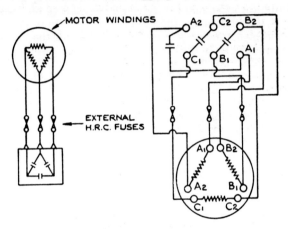

Fig. 6.—*Capacitor connections for individual power-factor control of induction motors*

Connection of the capacitors through fuses is preferred for protection and isolation. Fuse rating approximately 50 per cent. higher than capacitor current. Connections shown across the terminals of the star-delta starter allow power-factor improvement during starting as well as running.

Why can a capacitor be used for improving the power factor ?

Introducing inductance into an a.c. circuit causes the current to reach its maximum value later than the voltage. Introducing capacitance into an a.c. circuit causes the current to attain its maximum value earlier than the voltage. Therefore, by adding a suitable capacitor to an inductive circuit the time lag can be reduced by any desired amount.

17

Where are capacitors placed in an installation ?

The installation of a capacitor has the effect of decreasing the current taken from the supply but does not decrease the excitation current actively circulating round the capacitor-motor circuit. Theoretically, therefore, the best position for a capacitor is as near as possible to the motor, that is, directly across the motor terminals, thus allowing the use of a smaller size of feeder owing to the reduced current taken from the supply. However, it is not generally an economic arrangement to correct the power factor of each motor in an installation individually, unless they are large motors. This is because of the relatively high cost per kVA of capacitors in small sizes. It is often desirable to group small motors together for correction with a moderately-sized capacitor whose cost would be much less than a number of small capacitors of the same total kVA. The corrective equipment in such cases is installed either in groups distributed about the internal supply system or, in small compact installations, in a block connected at or near the point of supply.

When a capacitor is individually connected to a motor, it is controlled by the same switch as the motor so that it is always brought into service when required. Group or block connection of capacitors may require some method of control, as capacitance must be taken out of service when not required. The best type of control is automatic control.

How is the insulation resistance of a motor winding checked ?

With a 500-volt insulation-resistance tester. The insulation resistance in megohms should not be less than

$$\frac{\text{Motor rated voltage}}{1 + \text{rated kVA}}$$

If insulation resistance is low, what is the most likely cause ?

The presence of moisture in the windings.

How can motor windings be dried out ?

By placing the armature or stator concerned (not the complete machine) in an oven for about 12 hours at a temperature of 110°-120°C After the windings have cooled, the insulation should be rechecked.

What is the purpose of the motor enclosure ?

To protect the windings and bearings from the abrasive, destructive or corrosive effects of dust, liquid or gas in the surrounding atmosphere. A motor with inadequate protection will have its life greatly curtailed.

What is the effect of dust on the windings ?

The ventilation of the motor may be impeded and it will tend to overheat. If the dust is abrasive it will become embedded in the insulation and result in short circuits.

2

THREE-PHASE INDUCTION MOTORS

What is the phase sequence of the supply ?

The order in which the line voltages, measured from the star point, attain their immediately succeeding maximum values of the same sign (either positive or negative). The British standard sequence of 3-phase supply is L1, L2, and L3, or red, yellow (or white) and blue.

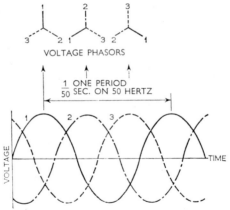

Fig. 7.—Phase-sequence of 3-phase supply

What is the basis of operation of all polyphase motors ?

The rotating magnetic field set up when the primary

windings of the motor are connected to an alternating-current supply.

What are the properties of this rotating magnetic field ?

(1) Direction of rotation.
(2) Speed of rotation.
(3) Magnitude of the field—with constant-voltage supply this remains substantially constant in the working range of the motor between no-load and full-load.

On what does the direction of rotation of an induction motor depend ?

On the phase sequence of the supply lines and the order in which these lines are connected to the stator windings.

What is the simplest form of motor ?

The induction motor. Electrical energy supplied to the circuits of the stationary member (termed the stator) is transferred inductively to the circuits of the rotating member (termed the rotor). The rotor is arranged inside the stator, separated by a small air gap. No electrical connection is necessary between the two sets of circuits.

How does the 3-phase induction motor operate ?

Each of the three lines of the supply are mutually displaced from each other by 120° (electrical—see Fig. 7. These lines are connected to three sets of windings as shown in Fig. 8 to form the primary windings of the motor and the three sets of windings will reach similar peak magnetism in phase sequence, resulting in a rotating magnetic field. The secondary windings on the rotor have an e.m.f. induced in them, resulting in a magnetic field around them. Interaction of the two magnetic fields provides a rotating torque.

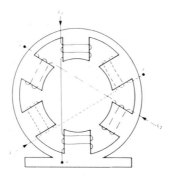

Fig. 8.—Production of the rotating field in a 3-phase induction motor. Note: Points X, Y and Z could be connected together to form a star point, i.e. star connection

How are the phases connected round the stator ?

Round the stator we have three-phase groups of conductors of one phase per pole. These groups follow the sequence A, B, C, if read a certain way round (usually clockwise) and the sequence is repeated as many times as there are numbers of poles. If now L1, L2 and L3 of standard phase sequence are connected to phases named A, B and C respectively, the motor will rotate in the reverse direction to the sequence of the phase groups (anticlockwise if the phase groups follow the sequence A, B, and C when read in a clockwise direction).

Fig. 9.—Line connection, phase groups, and rotation of a 3-phase 4-pole induction motor

Supply lines of standard phase sequence connected L1 to A. L2 to B and L3 to C phase groups. Rotation will be anticlockwise.

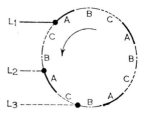

22

How are the stator and rotor cores constructed ?

Stator and rotor cores are built up from steel laminations with slots to receive the windings. The laminations are punched from high-quality electrical sheet steel, about 0·5 mm thick and lightly insulated with varnish, china clay or similar material on one or both sides. The purpose of the lamination is to reduce to the minimum the eddy currents set up by the alternating magnetic field. Large stators are built up with segmental stampings for ease of handling.

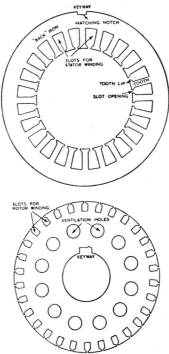

Fig. 10.—Stator and rotor laminations

How is the direction of rotation reversed ?

The direction of rotation is reversed by changing over any two connections of the supply lines to the windings.

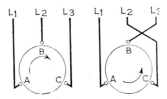

The direction of rotation is reversed by changing over any two connections of the supply lines

Fig. 11.—Reversing the direction of rotation.

What determines the speed of the rotating field ?

The number of poles in the motor and the frequency of the supply according to the formula:

$$\text{Revolutions per minute} = \frac{\text{Supply frequency} \times 60}{\text{No. of pairs of poles}}$$

This is termed the synchronous speed of the motor.

Does induction motor speed correspond to the synchronous speed ?

No, the speed of the rotating member of an induction motor is always less than that of the rotating field.

Why does the rotor of an induction motor rotate at a lower speed than the speed of the rotating field ?

To produce torque and therefore rotate, the rotor must be carrying a current. In the induction motor, this current arises in the rotor conductors because the rotating magnetic field cuts across and so generates voltages in them. The closer the rotor speed approaches field speed, the slower

24

the rate of cutting of the rotor conductors, the less the current induced in them and the smaller the torque produced. The consequence is that the rotor speed never reaches synchronous speed because at that speed no current would be flowing in the rotor conductors and therefore no torque would be produced.

The difference between synchronous speed and rotor speed is called the slip speed.

How is slip speed usually described ?

Slip speed is usually expressed as a percentage (sometimes as a fraction) of the synchronous speed. If, for example a 6-pole 50-Hz motor is running at 900 r.p.m. and the rotating field is moving at 1,000 r.p.m., the speed of the motor relative to the field is 1,000 − 900 r.p.m. = 100 r.p.m., a slip speed of 10 per cent of synchronous speed.

What is the size of the air gap between the stator and rotor ?

It ranges from 1·25 mm in small motors to 2·5 mm or more in large motors. The air gap is kept to the minimum possible for the reason that the more the gap the greater magnetising force required to establish a magnetic flux in it. It is also necessary to keep the gap uniform, which accounts for much of the mechanical rigidity of the shaft, frame and bedplate in a well designed motor.

What are the two principal kinds of induction motor ?

The squirrel-cage motor and the slip ring motor, depending on the type of rotor used.

How is the squirrel-cage rotor constructed ?

In the squirrel-cage motor, the rotor winding consists of a series of bars of aluminium, copper or other conductor, usually uninsulated, accommodated in the rotor-core slots, all bars being completely short-circuited at each end by a conducting ring. The starting and running characteristics of the motor are fixed by the design of the rotor winding.

What type of rotor winding is used in the slip-ring motor ?

In the slip-ring motor, the rotor has a winding very similar to that on the stator. The ends of the rotor winding are brought out to three slip rings, which allow the behaviour of the motor to be altered by introducing resistance into the rotor circuit.

On what does the starting torque of a squirrel-cage motor depend ?

On the design of its squirrel-cage rotor.

Why is the squirrel-cage motor the most widely used ?

Because it is the simplest, cheapest and most-robust type of motor and suitable for most drive requirements. Its rotor construction is without any slip-rings, commutator or brushes requiring maintenance.

What is the principal drawback of the squirrel-cage motor ?

The starting (or standstill) current has a high value relative to the starting torque, although plain squirrel-cage motors are much improved in this respect compared with a few years ago.

Another way of looking at it is that the starting torque is low relative to the current taken by the stator. Typical starting values are 150 per cent of full-load torque and 600 per cent of full-load current. The stator current is at a low power factor of about $0 \cdot 35$ at standstill. These values vary quite a bit between small and large machines, the smaller one behaving better since the natural resistance of the windings is proportionally higher.

What is meant by the pull-out torque of an induction motor?

The critical point on the torque-speed curve where the torque starts to fall off sharply, known as the pull-out or maximum torque. If the motor is loaded beyond this point, it will no longer take the load and the speed will fall quickly to zero. In the average induction motor this occurs at a load of 2 or 2½ times the normal full-load torque.

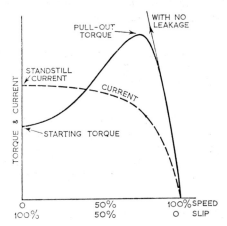

Fig. 12.—Rotor current-speed and torque-speed curves for a typical squirrel-cage-motor.

Stator-current characteristics are very similar. Starting current (about 6 times full-load current) is high relative to starting torque (about 150 per cent of full-load torque). Note maximum or pull-out torque which occurs at a load 2 to 2½ times full-load value.

What sort of squirrel-cage rotor gives both high starting and high running efficiencies?

A rotor having two squirrel-cage windings or a single cage operating on the current-displacement principle.

How does the double-cage rotor work?

The outer cage is of high resistance and current flowing in this provides the starting effort. The inner cage of relatively-low resistance carries little current during start (when the frequency is high), since it has a high reactance or choking effect due to the depth it is sunk in the rotor core. During starting, the current is displaced into the outer high-resistance cage in greater or less degree according to design. As the rotor runs up to speed, the frequency of the currents in it decreases. The choking effect of the inner cage, being determined by the frequency, becomes less and less until at running speed it becomes very small indeed.

For example, in a 50-Hz motor with a full-load slip of 2 per cent, the starting frequency in the rotor is 50 Hz, whilst at speed the frequency is only 1. This being so, the

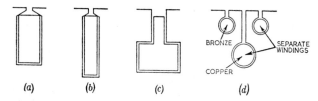

Fig. 13.—Types of squirrel-cage rotor conductors

(a) Normal.   (b) Deep-bar.   (c) Sash-bar.   (d) Double-cage

rotor current at full-speed is distributed in the two cages according to the resistance, and the rotor behaves like a normal squirrel-cage machine having the same total copper section.

In this way, a high-starting efficiency is obtained, due to the high-resistance outer cage acting more or less on its own, and a high-running efficiency when the two cages are carrying current in parallel with consequent low resistance and small rotor loss.

What other squirrel-cage constructions give the current-displacement effect?

Two forms of single-cage construction are shown. By using deep bars for the rotor winding, a certain degree of current displacement is possible. For example with a bar

28

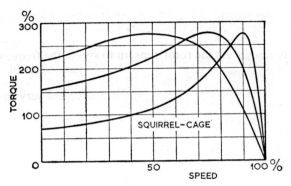

Fig. 14.—Torque-speed curves for various types of plain squirrel-cage motors

The higher the resistance of the cage, the better the starting torque.

25 mm. deep the resistance at 50 Hz (i.e. at start) is approximately $2\frac{1}{2}$ times the running value. By using a bar having an inverted T section or a sash bar, the deep-bar effect is enhanced and considerably higher 50-Hz resistance values can be attained. This simple and robust construction avoids the relative complication of the double-cage design

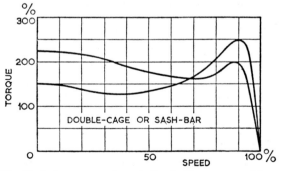

Fig. 15.—Typical torque-speed curves for double-cage or sash-bar-cage motors.

and is sufficient to satisfy a large proportion of the demand
for motors with high-starting efficiency.

What effect has the current-displacement rotor on pull-out torque and running power factor ?

Motors employing the current-displacement principle
have a rather lower pull-out torque and lower running
power factor than the corresponding plain squirrel-cage
motor.

What is a dual-voltage motor ?

An induction motor having its nameplate stamped with
two ranges of voltage (for example, 220/240 and 380/420
volts) and having six terminals.

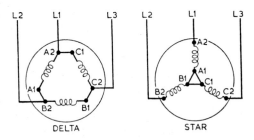

Fig. 16.—Dual-voltage induction motor

Its 3-phase windings are connected in delta for operation on lower voltage and
are connected in star for higher voltage.

The motor would be connected in delta for the lower
voltage range and in star for the higher voltage range.
The connections for the lower-voltage range would be
terminals A2, B2 and C2 to the supply while the following
terminals would be joined: A2 and C1, B2 and A1, C2
and B1. For the higher-voltage range, terminals A2, B2
and C2 would be connected to the supply and terminals
A1, B1 and C1 would be joined for the star connection.

What is a high-slip motor ?

A variation of the squirrel-cage motor having a high-resistance rotor; instead of copper or aluminium for the rotor windings, a material of higher resistance is employed, such as bronze. The result is an increase in the starting torque per ampere and a greater reduction in speed, or higher slip, with increase in load.

With a bronze rotor winding having twice the resistance of copper, the starting torque is nearly doubled for the same, or slightly less, starting current than with a copper winding. At the same time, the running slip and the loss in the rotor is increased, resulting in a fall in efficiency and an increase in temperature rise. Consequently it is necessary to have a larger motor to carry the extra loss.

A slip-ring motor with its external rotor resistance permanently connected in circuit also acts as a high-slip motor. This is more efficient because the extra heat loss is largely dissipated outside the motor, enabling a smaller motor to be employed.

What are the applications of a high-slip motor ?

Where the load is intermittent and comes on very sharply for brief periods, such as a punching machine. A heavy flywheel is fitted in the drive, preferably between the work and any speed-reduction gears. The flywheel shares the load with the motor, thus enabling a motor of lower rating to be employed. For load sharing to take place automatically, the motor speed should drop considerably as the load increases and this is ensured by using a motor having a high full-load slip, say 10 per cent.

What are the effects of inserting resistance in the rotor circuit of an induction motor ?

The motor speed can be varied by varying the amount of resistance, and the starting torque is improved.

Why does speed reduce when resistance is inserted in the rotor circuit ?

Extra resistance in the rotor circuit means that it is necessary for a higher voltage to be generated across the windings than in the short-circuited rotor in order to circulate the same current. This voltage is only generated at a lower speed, that is, at a higher slip. In general, the insertion of a resistance across the slip-rings gives the torque required at a lower speed. In fact, when the total resistance in the rotor windings, including that of the

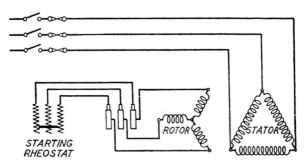

Fig. 17.—Three-phase slip-ring-motor connections

The rotor windings are connected to slip rings, enabling resistance to be inserted n the rotor circuit. The variable external rotor resistors across the slip rings allow control of starting performance and speed.

winding itself, is doubled, the slip at which full-load torque is obtained is also doubled.

Why is the starting torque improved when resistance is inserted in the rotor circuit ?

Because of the increase of resistance compared with the reactance of the rotor windings. The rotor currents attain their maximum values more nearly coincident with the maximum values of the magnetic field producing them and, consequently, at any given speed a much greater torque is obtained.

What are the disadvantages of using a slip-ring motor for speed control ?

One disadvantage is that the efficiency is reduced when running with resistance across the slip-rings. For example, if the speed is reduced to one-half, the efficiency is also halved, because half the power of the motor is wasted in the form of heat in the rotor resistance.

The second disadvantage is that if the load is removed the speed returns to nearly synchronous speed. Consequently, with fluctuating load the motor speed rises and falls appreciably.

The energy losses when operating at reduced speeds are so considerable that the use of the slip-ring motor for obtaining speed variation is limited. Their variable-speed application is generally confined to duties requiring operation at low speeds for only brief periods, such as for hoists, or where only a small speed variation is required, as in pump and fan drives, where the fluid or air delivery falls off quickly with a small reduction of speed.

How are slip rings arranged on the motor shaft ?

Slip rings, usually of hard-wearing phosphor-bronze or copper-nickel, are shrunk on to a micanite-insulated bush which is pressed on the motor shaft; in small motors a moulded type of insulation may be used for ease of production.

The rings may be mounted internally or externally to the motor bearing. When mounted externally, the leads from the rotor winding are carried through a hole drilled in the motor shaft.

Where possible, some degree of ventilation is given to the rings, the enclosing cover having small openings for this purpose. Totally-enclosed rings are desirable if working in an atmosphere laden with abrasive dust. Flameproof enclosure is specified when working in an explosive atmosphere.

How is brush gear for slip rings arranged ?

Brushes consist of various special mixtures of copper or bronze and graphite. Pressure on the brushes is applied through spring fingers, usually arranged to lock back for ease in removing the brushes. Current from the brushes is carried by firmly-attached flexible leads.

In some cases, slip rings are arranged so that they are short-circuited after performing their starting function. One method of doing this is to use a short-circuiting collar which rotates with but is free to slide on the motor shaft, the collar being operated by a handle located on the outside of the housing.

In addition to short-circuiting gear, another feature sometimes specified is brush-lifting gear, which positively ensures that no brush wear occurs in the "run" position. With brush-lifting gear it is usual for the short-circuiting handle to have an electrical contact interlocked with the rotor-resistance starter to make starting impossible unless the handle is in the correct position.

How are windings assembled in the slots ?

The methods used for introducing the coils into the slots can be divided into two main classes: drop-in and push-through windings.

In the drop-in class, the individual wires of the coil side are dropped one or a few turns at a time into the slot through a relatively small opening (partially-closed slot). The slot insulation is then folded over a wedge driven along the top of the slot to keep the conductors secure.

There is a variation of this, used mainly for high-tension stators, where the coil is completely pre-formed with the slot insulation moulded round the coil legs. The mouth of the slot is practically as wide as the remainder (open slot). This method of winding has distinct merits in manufacture and repair, but requires careful design to compete in power factor and efficiency with a motor having partially-closed slots.

Push-through windings include bar windings and hairpin windings.

The push-through bar winding is made from straight copper strips with insulation on the slot portion, forming a half coil. One end is bent to end-winding shape. The half-coil is then pushed through the slot, bent at the other end, and joined at both ends to the appropriate adjacent bars to form the winding.

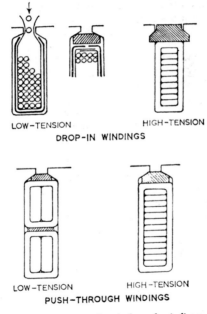

LOW-TENSION   HIGH-TENSION

DROP-IN WINDINGS

LOW-TENSION   HIGH-TENSION

PUSH-THROUGH WINDINGS

Fig. 18.—Drop-in and push-through windings.

The hairpin winding, which is an alternative to the open-slot winding for high-tension machines, consists of from 5 to 20 or more turns per coil. Each coil is pre-formed, cut through at one end, insulated round the slot portion and bent to shape at one end. The two legs are then pushed through the slots and the coil ends formed on a block, to exact length and welded individually. They can also be joined by soldered clips.

What insulation is required in a motor ?

(1) Covering for the conductors in the coils.

(2) Coil insulation in the slots, comprising liners for the slots and, if more than one coil side is laid in the slots, separators between coil sides.

(3) End-winding insulation, comprising tapes or separators.

(4) Varnish impregnation, filling spaces inside the slots, holding wires in place and excluding moisture and other contaminants.

What is the life expectation of insulation ?

When operating continuously at the maximum temperature of its class, the life expectation is seven years. Most

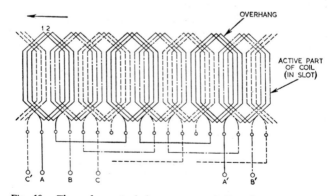

Fig. 19.—Three-phase single-layer stator winding for 6-pole motor.

A single-layer winding has one coil side in each slot, i.e. it has half as many coils as there are slots. The above winding has 3 slots per pole per phase, a total of 54 slots.

36

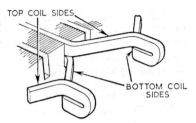

Fig. 20.—Arrangement of coils of double-layer winding.

In a double-layer winding, each slot contains two coil sides. Each coil has one side in the top of a slot and the other side in the bottom of a different slot.

BOTTOM COIL SIDES

motors, however, do not operate under these extreme conditions and for these the probable life is around 15 to 20 years. For the more onerous duties, the same result is achieved by using a class of insulation operating 10°C under its maximum temperature, for example Class B running at Class E temperature.

How are the stator windings arranged in the slots ?

The stator winding is rarely concentrated into one coil per pole in each phase, but is distributed in the slots around the stator in two or more coils per pole in each phase. There may be as many coils as there are slots, in the stator or, alternatively, only half as many coils as slots.

For the simpler case of half as many coils as there are slots, it will be a single-layer winding using one coil side to each slot, each coil spanning a number of slots equivalent to the pole pitch.

For the case where there are as many coils as there are slots it will be a double-layer winding using two coil sides to each slot.

How are the end-windings arranged ?

The overhang of each coil at the ends of the stator core has to span a number of slots depending on the pole pitch. End windings have to be formed to do this while crossing over each other in the limited space available. There are a great number of ways in which the end windings can be arranged. The main types are shown in the accompanying diagrams.

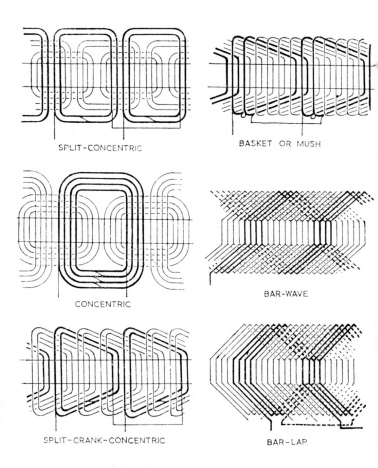

SPLIT-CONCENTRIC

BASKET OR MUSH

CONCENTRIC

BAR-WAVE

SPLIT-CRANK-CONCENTRIC

BAR-LAP

Fig. 21.—Ways in which coils can be arranged to give the necessary span.

The bar-wave and bar-lap windings are double-layer, the bottom coils sides being shown dotted. All the above windings are 4 slots per pole per phase.

Among the points to be considered are: ease of manufacture, accessibility for repair, provision of insulation
clearances (especially in high-tension machines) and suit-
ability for bracing against switching stresses. The last is
particularly important for large squirrel-cage motors or
for any motors that are stopped or reversed by "plugging".

What types of wire insulation are commonly used ?

Synthetic-enamel coverings are now widely used, largely
replacing cotton and silk and to a lesser extent asbestos
and glass.

If a motor is required to operate on a voltage different from that for which it was designed, what would it be necessary to do ?

Alter the number of conductors per slot in the same
ratio as the change in voltage. For example, to double
the voltage, double the conductors per slot.

Is it possible to change the power of an induction motor?

In many cases, motors are designed so that their magnetic parts are approaching saturation and it will not be
possible to increase the power except when converting
totally-enclosed motors to the open type.

The number of conductors per slot must be altered
inversely as the square root of the power.

Is it practical to rewind an induction motor for the same power on a different frequency?

The conductors per slot are altered inversely as the
square root of the change in frequency. In such cases,
however, the speed changes in proportion to the frequency
and when rewinding for a *lower* frequency the reduced
speed may mean that the cooling and the magnetic circuit
are not adequate for the full power on the lower speed.

INDUCTION-MOTOR CONTROL GEAR

What are the main functions of control gear ?

(1)   To provide a means of starting and stopping the motor and, at the same time, of limiting the starting current if required.

(2)   To give adequate protection of the motor under all conditions.

(3)   To allow of speed changing when required.

(4)   To provide means of braking the motor when required.

(5)   To reverse the direction of rotation when required.

Protection of the motor must be automatic, but the other operations may be arranged to be under the control of an operator, or may be partly or fully-automatic.

What devices are required to give adequate protection to the motor ?

(1)   Under-voltage release to prevent automatic re-starting after a stoppage due to a drop in voltage or failure of the supply, where unexpected restarting of the motor might cause injury to an operator.

(2)   Overload relays for protection against excessive current in the motor windings—for example, in the event of overload or failure of the motor.

What provision must be made for short-circuit conditions in motor circuits ?

Since overload relays are not designed to operate and

clear the circuit in the event of a short-circuit, circuit-breaker or fuse protection of sufficient breaking capacity to deal with any possible short-circuit that may occur must be provided.

What are the usual forms of overload relay in motor-control gear ?

In small contactor starters, generally thermal relays, either of the "solder pot" or bi-metal type. With large contactors or oil switches magnetic relays of the solenoid type with dashpots. Either type of overload relay may be met with in intermediate sizes.

How do thermal relays work?

The bimetallic thermal relay consists of a small bimetallic strip that is heated by an element connected in series with the supply. When the current rises above a preset value, the movement of the strip releases a catch which opens the trip contacts.

How does the magnetic overload relay operate?

A solenoid connected in series with the supply contains a plunger whose movement is damped by a dashpot. When the safe current is exceeded, the solenoid pulls the plunger up—disconnecting the supply. The damping provided by the dashpot prevents unwarranted tripping on short-time over-loads.

How many overload relays are required in the control gear?

On 3-phase supplies where the neutral point of the system is connected to earth, as is usually the case, three overload relays one in each line are necessary for complete protection.

For 2-phase 3-wire and 4-wire supplies two overload relays are required, one in each phase line, none being connected in any neutral or earth conductor.

With single-phase motors one overload relay in any conductor except an earthed conductor or neutral.

What happens when one of the three lines supplying a 3-phase induction motor becomes open-circuited?

The motor, if already running, will continue to run as a single-phase motor on the remaining single-phase supply. The condition is called single-phasing. If the motor is loaded to more than about 30 per cent of full load, the currents in the motor windings tend to become excessive and overheating occurs.

With one line broken, the motor will not start up and, due to the heavy standstill current, burn-out is likely unless the motor is quickly disconnected.

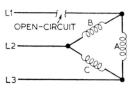

Fig. 22.—Open-circuited supply line of delta-connected motor.

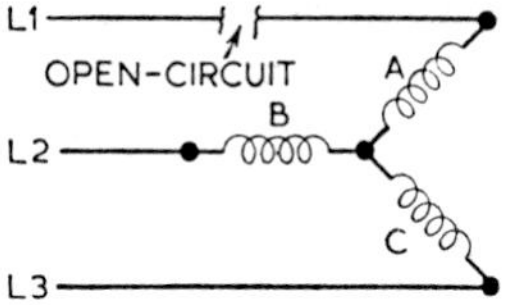

Fig. 23.—Open-circuited supply line of star-connected motor.

What currents flow in a single-phasing delta-connected motor ?

Assuming that supply line L1 is open-circuited, as shown, typical line and phase currents, given as percentages of normal full-load 3-phase current, at various loads will be

| | Percentage of full load current at | | |
	½ load	¾ load	Full load
Lines L2 and L3	98	155	250
Phase C	118	187	285
Phases A and B	55	90	147

Thus, phase C connected across the two operative lines carries nearly three times normal current under single-phasing conditions at full load, while phases A and B, which are in series, carry more than full-load current.

What currents flow in a single-phasing star-connected motor ?

Assuming that line L1 is open-circuited, as shown, the current flowing at full load in lines L2 and L3 and through the two phases in series will be of the order of 250 per cent of normal full-load current, 155 per cent on $\frac{3}{4}$-load and 98 per cent on $\frac{1}{2}$-load.

Will normal overload relays trip on single-phasing ?

If correctly set, the normal overloads will trip when the motor is fully loaded due to the rise in current passing through the closed supply lines. With a delta-connected motor partially loaded, the rise in line current may not be sufficient to operate the overload trip and one phase may become excessively overheated.

What special protection can be provided against single-phasing ?

One method is to incorporate a combined overload and single-phase relay in the control gear. A typical relay of this type includes three overload relays with trip contacts so arranged that it will trip if the displacement of one overload element differs from that of the others. This type of relay will operate if single-phasing occurs at or near full load with the same time delay as on overload, but at light loads, the time delay for single-phase protection is longer.

Another device is a phase-failure relay in the control gear. Its principle is based on the fact that the currents in the supply lines or the voltages between them at the motor terminals are unbalanced when the motor is single-phasing. The phase-failure relay may be of the current- or voltage-operated type which trips out the line switch when one of the supply lines becomes open-circuited.

What are alternatives to the use of overload releases ?

Direct protection against overheating or burning-out

of motor windings may be built into the motor. Built-in protectors may take the form of thermostats or thermistors embedded in the end-windings of the stator while the motor is under construction. These devices are sensitive to the winding temperatures and are arranged in a suitable circuit so as to cause the motor to be switched off if the windings heat up excessively.

How are built-in thermostatic overload protectors arranged?

Built-in thermostatic protectors, or BITOPS as they are called, are tiny thermostats, each with two contacts, embedded in the end-windings of the motor. It is usual to place a BITOP in one coil of each of the three phase windings and to wire them in series so that the contacts carry the current of the starter-contactor coil. This arrangement protects against single-phasing as well as providing overload protection.

One eventuality against which BITOPS alone cannot guard is an attempt to start the motor from cold with the shaft jammed against an impossible load, that is, the locked rotor condition. In this condition, the thermostats cannot act quickly enough. If this situation is to be countered, additional protection has to be employed to deal with it. One manufacturer employs reinforced insulation in the end-windings.

How do built-in thermistors work ?

Thermistors are very small semiconductor devices whose resistance changes rapidly with temperature. Three thermistors are inserted in the end-windings of the stator, one in each phase, and are connected in series. The two thermistor terminals at the motor are connected to an electronic-amplifier-control unit in the starter, through which the tripping circuit of the starter is operated. The response of the thermistors to temperature change is extremely rapid, allowing this type of protection to be effective under all motor-overload conditions.

When is direct-on-line starting used for 3-phase squirrel-cage motors ?

It is usual for small machines; for larger motors it is often necessary to use other methods of starting in order to avoid excessive starting currents.

What are the connections for direct-on-line starters ?

The scheme of connections is merely three line leads in

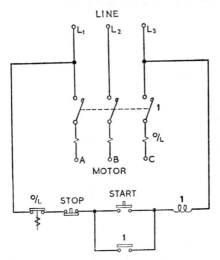

Fig. 24.—Basic circuit of direct-on-line contactor starter for squirrel-cage motor

1 indicates the contactor coil and the contacts operated by
it when it is energised.

and three motor leads out. Direct-on-line contactor starters are designed round the basic circuit shown. An isolating switch may be incorporated in the starter. If reversing is required, two contactors one for each rotation, are required and are interlocked so that only one can close at a time.

A hand-operated oil switch with under-voltage trip coil may be used with larger motors.

What methods are employed to reduce the starting current of squirrel-cage motors ?

Where the starting conditions are light, the starting

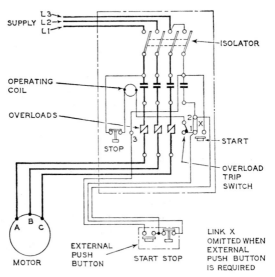

Fig. 25.—Connection diagram for direct-on-line contactor starter.

current can be lessened by some method of reducing the stator voltage when switching on. There are four ways of starting on reduced voltage:

(1) Primary-resistance starting—introducing resistance between the supply and the stator windings.

(2) Primary-reactor starting—introducing a reactor in series with the stator windings, usually connected in the star point.

46

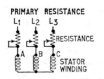

Fig 26. — Primary-re-sistance and primary-reactor methods of re-duced-voltage starting for squirrel-cage motors

PRIMARY RESISTANCE
L1 L2 L3
RESISTANCE
A B C
STATOR WINDING

PRIMARY REACTOR
L1 L2 L3
A2 B2 C2
STATOR WINDING
A1 B1 C1
REACTOR

(3) Star-delta starting—connecting the stator windings in star for starting and in delta for running.

(4) Auto-transformer starting—supplying the stator windings through tappings on an auto-transformer.

When is primary-resistance starting employed ?

Generally, only for small motors on light-starting duty. The method is easily adjustable to suit the load and gives a smooth breakaway against low torque. If the resistance is adjustable, as in a face-plate starter, starting can be very smooth and this is useful for motors that must be started without any shock that might cause injury to the material being handled by the driven machine.

When is the primary reactor method of starting employed?

Mainly for high-tension motors on very light-starting load where a fairly heavy starting current can be per-mitted—for example boiler-feed pumps in a large power station.

Fig. 27.—Star-delta methods of reduced-voltage starting for squirrel-cage motors.

Showing the switching sequence for plain and Wauchope methods.

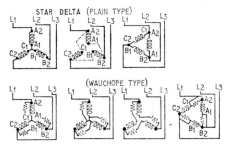

STAR DELTA (PLAIN TYPE)

(WAUCHOPE TYPE)

47

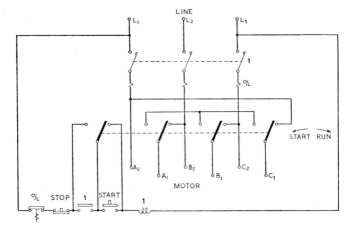

Fig. 28.—Basic circuit of star-delta starter employing line contactor and hand-operated start-run switch.

The start button must be depressed until the switch is moved into the "run" position. 1 indicates contactor coil, line switch and maintaining contacts operated by the contactor coil.

When is the star-delta starter used ?

When the starting current has to be reduced and starting current and torque values one-third of those obtained with direct-on-line starting are suitable. It is necessary that the motor be designed to operate with the primary winding connected in delta, but with six terminals brought out to allow for connection in star during starting.

The plain star-delta method is used for small and medium-size motors on light-starting loads, for example centrifugal pumps, fans having low inertia, line shafting and motor-generator sets.

The Wauchope-type has the same uses but prevents the drop in speed when the stator is disconnected from the supply in changing from star to delta. Switching is done through resistances to maintain continuous line contact.

48

This also obviates the momentary high current when switching from star to delta.

What are the connections for a star-delta starter ?

Motors arranged for star-delta starting have six terminals—the two ends of each phase winding being brought out to terminals marked A1, B1, C1 and A2, B2, C2. These terminals are connected to similarly-marked terminals in the starter.

The basic circuit of a typical hand-operated air-break or oil-immersed starter is shown in the diagram, the incoming supply being controlled by a line contactor. With the change-over switch in the start position, the motor windings are connected in star (A1, B1 and C1

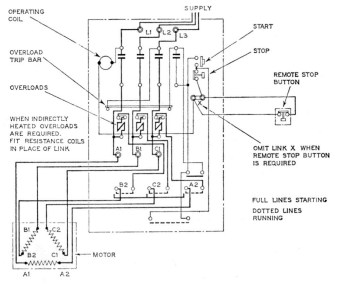

Fig. 29.—Connection diagram of air-break hand-operated star-delta starter with line-contactor.

together) and in the running position in delta (A2 to C1, B2 to A1 and C2 to B1). In starting the motor, the handle of the change-over switch is put into the start position, as indicated, and the "start" button is pressed. This energises the contactor coil which closes the triple-pole main switch and auxiliary switch (1). Note that the contactor coil cannot be energised unless the change-over switch has been placed in the "start" position.

When the motor has reached full speed, which is noticeable by sound, the handle of the change-over switch is moved to the "run" position and the "start" button is released. The motor is now directly connected to the line.

In some star-delta starters, the overload units are by-passed in the "start" position. A complete connection diagram of a hand-operated star-delta starter with this feature is also shown. Apart from the fact that the over-load units are brought into circuit only in the "run" position, the circuit is the same as the basic circuit.

A fully-automatic star-delta starter has two contactors and a triple-pole line contactor with time-delay relay between "start" and "run" connections.

When is an auto-transformer starter used ?

When more flexibility is required for starting a squirrel-cage motor than is provided by the star-delta method, which is limited as far as starting torque is concerned. Auto-transformer starting permits the stator to be wound for running in star. The starting torque can be adjusted to suit the load by changing the voltage tapping on the auto-transformer. Both starting torque and current are reduced in the same proportion.

It is used for motors of medium and large size on light starting loads (for example, centrifugal pumps, fans, compressors and mills). Up to about 75 kW the simple auto-transformer starter is employed; above this, the Korndorfer connection is recommended.

What does the simple auto-transformer starter consist of ?

The basic diagram is shown. The motor is started by connecting its primary to tappings on the starting transformer; then after a time delay, re-connecting direct to the supply. The winding on each limb of the auto-transformer usually has three taps, 40, 60 and 75 per cent of line voltage, but taps to give other percentages may be arranged as required. The auto-transformer may be used

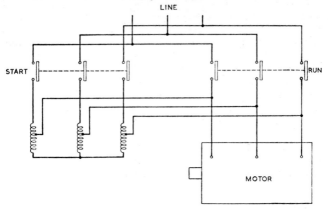

Fig. 30.—Basic diagram of auto-transformer starter for squirrel-cage motor.

in conjunction with a contactor panel, or alternatively a hand-operated switch.

The accompanying illustration shows the wiring diagram of an auto-transformer starter consisting of a line contactor interlocked with a hand-operated change-over switch, three thermal or magnetic overload relays and an auto-transformer.

What are the connections for the Korndorfer system ?

The simple auto-transformer starter has the disadvantage that at the instant of transition from "start" to "run"

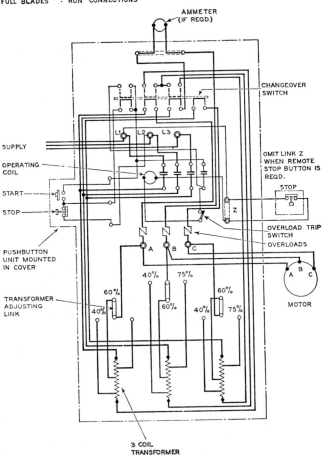

DOTTED BLADES : "START" CONNECTIONS
FULL BLADES : "RUN" CONNECTIONS

AMMETER
(IF REQD.)

CHANGEOVER
SWITCH

L1 L2 L3

SUPPLY

OPERATING
COIL

OMIT LINK Z
WHEN REMOTE
STOP BUTTON IS
REQD.

STOP

START

STOP

Z

OVERLOAD TRIP
SWITCH
OVERLOADS

PUSHBUTTON
UNIT MOUNTED
IN COVER

A   B   C

A B C

40%   75%

TRANSFORMER
ADJUSTING
LINK

60%

60%

MOTOR

40%

60%

40%   75%

3 COIL
TRANSFORMER

Fig. 31.—Connection diagram for air-break hand-operated auto-transformer starter with line contactor

the supply to the motor is interrupted. This means that the insulation may be stressed by high transient voltages.

The Korndorfer method keeps the motor connected to the supply continuously by means of the connections shown in the diagram. On the first step (a), switches 1 and 2 close and the motor accelerates at a reduced voltage

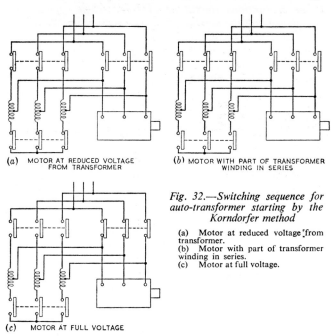

(a) MOTOR AT REDUCED VOLTAGE
        FROM TRANSFORMER

(b) MOTOR WITH PART OF TRANSFORMER
        WINDING IN SERIES

Fig. 32.—Switching sequence for auto-transformer starting by the Korndorfer method

(a) Motor at reduced voltage from transformer.
(b) Motor with part of transformer winding in series.
(c) Motor at full voltage.

(c) MOTOR AT FULL VOLTAGE

determined by the transformer tapping. On the second step (b), the star point of the transformer (switch 2) is opened so that the motor continues to run with part of the transformer winding in circuit. Next, this part is short-circuited by the "run" contactor or switch (switch 3 closes) and finally the "start" contactor or switch (1) is

53

opened, as shown at (c). A fully-automatic starter would comprise a triple-pole line contactor, start contactor, running contactor, three single-pole over-load relays, auto-transformer with a set of links for tap-changing, a suitable timer, and "start" and "stop" pushbuttons.

What precautions should be observed when applying reduced voltage starting to a load with rising characteristic such as fans ?

If the specified starting current is too low, the motor may start correctly but not run fully up to speed. The result is that on changing over to the running or full-voltage condition a very high current may be taken, thus negativing the low initial current. For this reason, even with fan drives, it is not desirable to pin the starting current lower than about 200 per cent of full-load current.

What are the initial-starting line current and motor torque when star-delta starting ?

Both line current and torque are approximately one-third of the motor standstill values on full volts.

What are the initial starting line current and motor torque when starting with primary resistance or primary reactance ?

The initial starting line current is approximately equal to

$$\frac{\text{applied voltage}}{\text{full voltage}} \times \text{standstill current with full volts.}$$

The initial starting torque is approximately equal to

$$\left(\frac{\text{applied voltage}}{\text{full voltage}}\right)^2 \times \text{standstill torque with full volts.}$$

What are the initial-starting line current and motor torque when starting by auto-transformer ?

The initial starting line current is approximately equal to

$$1 \cdot 1 \times \left(\frac{\text{applied voltage}}{\text{full voltage}}\right)^2 \times \text{standstill current with full}$$

volts.

The factor of $1 \cdot 1$ in the above allows for the magnetising current of the auto-transformer.

The initial starting torque is approximately equal to $\left(\frac{\text{applied voltage}}{\text{full voltage}}\right)^2 \times$ standstill torque with full volts.

Why are the above values of initial-starting current and torque approximate ?

Because the formulae given assume for simplicity that the standstill reactance of a motor is constant at all voltages—that the short-circuit current varies in direct proportion to the applied voltage. Owing to magnetic saturation, particularly of the slot lips, the standstill reactance tends to be less on full volts than on reduced volts so the current and torque values tend to be rather less than those obtained by the formulae given.

How do the various methods of starting on reduced voltage compare as regards torque per ampere ?

Star-delta and auto-transformer methods have the advantage over primary resistance and primary reactor methods.

What mechanical methods of reducing starting current can be adopted ?

The starting duty can be reduced by fitting a centrifugal or other type of clutch which only picks up the load when the motor is well up to speed.

What is sequence starting ?

A system of starting by which several motors of similar rating are started in sequence off one starter in conjunction with interlocked switching.

How does the control gear for 2-phase motors differ from 3-phase ?

The control gear is similar except that series-parallel starting is used instead of star-delta starting of squirrel-cage motors. Each phase of the stator winding is in halves which are connected in series for starting and in parallel for running, using either contactor control or a hand-operated switch.

Where reversal of rotation is required, the control gear must be connected to interchange the two outers of a 2-phase 3-wire system or to reverse one phase of a 2-phase 4-wire system.

How is a 2-phase induction motor reversed ?

A 2-phase motor connected to a 2-phase 4-wire supply is reversed by inter-changing at the starter the leads of one pair of phase lines to the motor.

Reversing a 2-phase 3-wire motor, in which one lead is common to both phases, is carried out by changing over the two outers at the starter.

How are slip-ring motors started ?

By first switching the supply on to the stator winding with all the external rotor resistance in circuit across the slip rings and then cutting out the rotor resistance progressively as the motor speeds up until finally the rotor winding is short-circuited.

What is the usual arrangement of connections for a hand-operated slip-ring starter ?

Small slip-ring starters usually consist of a contactor for the stator circuit and a face plate-type starting resistance for the rotor circuit. The basic essentials are shown, the three wires from the starter going to slip-ring terminals D, E and F on the motor. An actual wiring diagram is also shown. The starter must be fitted with interlocks to ensure that the resistance is all-in when starting. With a contactor controlling the stator supply, interlocking is simply effected, as shown, through electrical contacts on the arm of the rotor starter, no current reaching the contactor coil 1 unless the arm is in the starting position. The start button must be kept depressed until all resistance has been taken out; this ensures that the motor

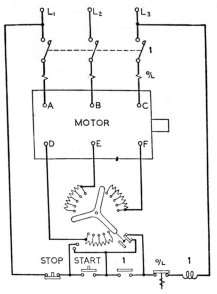

Fig. 33.—Basic diagram of contactor starter for slip-ring motor with faceplate-type secondary resistance

1 indicates contactor coil and contacts operated by the contactor coil.

is not accidentally left running with some of the rotor resistance still in circuit. When the operating arm of the faceplate is in the "run" position the start button is short-circuited.

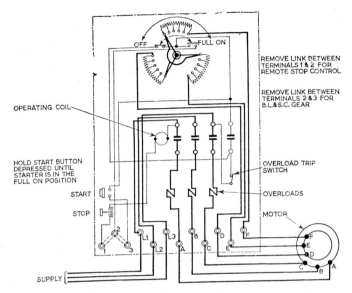

Fig. 34.—Connections of air-break stator-rotor starter

If the motor is fitted with a device designed to lift the brushes and short-circuit the slip rings when the motor is up to speed, an interlock must be arranged in the control circuit to ensure that the brush-gear is in the starting position before the stator contactor can close.

For larger motors, a stator oil switch is usual and may be used in conjunction with a liquid resistance or an oil-immersed grid resistance in the rotor circuit.

What are the essentials of a full-automatic stator-rotor starter ?

An automatic starter would include a triple-pole contactor to control the stator circuit, together with rotor-resistance grids short-circuited by the necessary number

58

of accelerating contactors, the last of which must be continuously rated to carry the full-load rotor current.

Also required are the necessary number of overload relays and timers controlling the duration of the starting period. The number of timers and accelerating contactors correspond to the number of steps of rotor resistance that are provided.

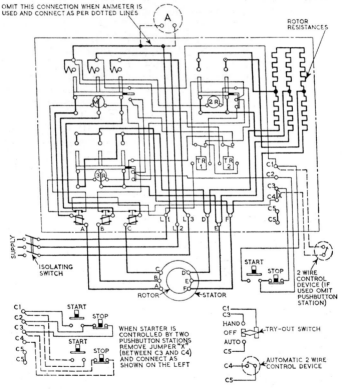

Fig. 35.—Connections of automatic slip-ring motor starter.

59

A wiring diagram of an automatic slip-ring-motor starter with two steps of rotor resistance is shown.

Control terminals are provided for push-button control from one or two positions, or alternatively, for automatic control (for use with thermostat, float-switch, time-switch or similar switching) with or without a try-out switch.

When the "start" button is pressed (or the automatic switch closes), the control circuit is made through the coil of the stator contactor M. The stator contactor closes, connecting the stator to the line. At the same time the first timing relay is TR1 is energised. At this stage, the rotor is completed through the whole resistance since the accelerating contactors 2R and 3R are open. After an adjustable delay, the contacts of TR1 close, thus energising the accelerating contactor 2R which short-circuits a portion of the rotor resistance and energising the second timing relay TR2. When in turn the contacts of TR2 close the second and, in this case, final contactor 3R is energised and closes, short-circuiting the whole of the rotor resistance. The overload relays are in circuit during starting and running. For automatic (2-wire) remote control, hand-resetting overloads are essential.

How is speed control of a slip-ring motor effected ?

By introducing resistance into the rotor circuit similar to a starting resistance except that the heat losses in the resistance must be dissipated continuously. Unless the duty is intermittent, all except small sizes require some means of cooling the resistors. Grid resistances with a motor-driven fan may be used in conjunction with a drum controller. Alternative methods are oil-immersed resistances or a liquid resistance cooled by circulating water through cooling tubes.

What is liquid resistance ?

Insulated pots filled with a resistance solution or electrolyte, for example, caustic soda or washing soda. Plates connected to the slip rings dip into the pots and are shorted

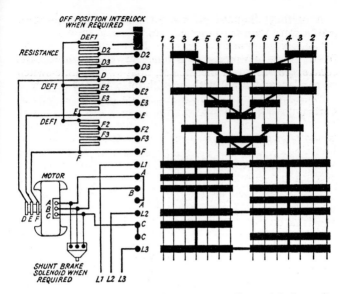

Fig. 36.—Connections of reversing-drum controller and 3-phase slip-ring motor.

The controller gives speed control by varying resistance in series with the rotor windings and also breaks the three stator phases in the "off" position. The moving-copper-contact rings are shown as thick horizontal lines, while the forward and reverse steps are indicated by the numbered vertical lines. The diagram below shows the connections of series limit switches when used.

Connections or series limit switches used with reversing-drum controller and 3-phase slip-ring motor.
Limit switches should be of the double-pole type breaking two phases

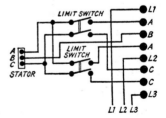

out in the full-speed position. Liquid starters and controllers are used for large motors.

*What is the advantage of a liquid resistance for starting
    purposes ?*

Resistance may be reduced continuously so that, with close control over the current as indicated on a ammeter, a very smooth start can be obtained.

What is a slip resistance ?

A fixed step of rotor resistance used to limit the current taken from the supply at the instant when peak load is applied to the motor. It is often desirable to do this on press drives, guillotines, etc. As the resistance value is small, it is usual to have a conventional starter so arranged that the last step of resistance is not cut out when the starting handle is right home. This last step of resistance is continuously rated.

What is meant by motors in synchronous tie ?

When two slip-ring motors are required to run at the same speed, it is possible to do this by connecting their rotors together through the slip rings in conjunction with a single slip resistance. The starter for such a scheme includes a single rotor resistance, the last step of which is the continuously-rated slip resistance, and two stator contactors, one for each motor. In order to limit the circulating current in the event of the motors being out of phase when started, a reactance is usually inserted in the interconnecting tie. The reactor is wound in two sections, and connected so that it is non-inductive to currents flowing through each half into the slip resistance but inductive to circulating currents between rotors. This reactance also assists load sharing when the two motors are driving a common load, as for example travel motors at opposite ends of an overhead crane.

4

BRAKING OF A.C. MOTORS

When is braking of an electric motor required ?

When there is a need to bring a drive quickly to rest, to hold a drive at standstill after some operation has been completed, or to check the speed rise of a motor with an overhauling load.

What are the principal ways of braking electric motors ?

By mechanical braking, by arranging the motor itself to exert a braking torque, or a combination of the two methods.

With mechanical braking, a drum or disc friction-type brake is usual, the brake shoes being held off against spring loading by a solenoid or electrically-operated thrustor gear normally connected across the motor terminals.

Apart from mechanical braking, there are three principal methods:

(1) Regenerative braking, applied to overhauling loads; it can only be used to reduce the speed to the no-load or synchronous value.

(2) Counter-current braking or plugging, achieved by reconnecting the machine so that its output torque reverses.

(3) Dynamic braking, obtained by disconnecting the machine from the mains and establishing a fixed magnetic field from a d.c. supply which causes e.m.f.s. to be induced

in the rotating windings. Powerful dynamic braking may be obtained by introducing capacitors into an induction-motor circuit, with or without d.c. injection.

How is plugging applied to a.c. motors ?

The phase sequence of the supply (in the case of 3-phase) is reversed by interchanging two leads. The usual arrangement for squirrel-cage motors is by a reverse contactor which closes when the stop button is operated. The supply to the motor must be disconnected as the speed nears zero. This is effected by having a reverse-rotation relay coupled to the motor shaft and connected to open the braking-contactor coil before the motor reverses. The motor takes heavy current from the supply unless resistance is added to the stator circuit. Rotor resistance may be employed to ensure that a high braking torque is obtained.

Plugging is the commonest braking method used with Schrage type a.c. commutator motors. With this type, provision must be made in the control gear to insert a resistance in each secondary phase during plugging to limit current to a safe value.

How is d.c.-injection braking applied to induction motors ?

Direct current is injected into the stator winding after this winding has been disconnected from the supply.

This sets up a stationary field, inducing e.m.f.s and hence currents in the rotor circuits. The method provides a high-braking torque with low losses, but the braking effect is small at high speeds for machines of normal slip and it is usually necessary to use heavy d.c. exciting currents to effect a quick stop. Some improvement of the braking characteristic can be made by increasing the rotor-circuit resistance at high speeds and reducing it as the speed falls.

The control gear must include a transformer and rectifier to give a low-voltage heavy-current d.c. which is applied to the motor windings when the stop button is operated. If secondary resistance is included to increase the available braking torque, provision for this is required. The direct current is usually disconnected after a time delay. Direct-current-injection braking has the advantage over plugging that reversal of the motor cannot take place.

Can d.c.-injection braking be applied to other types of a.c. motor ?

It is commonly applied to stator-fed shunt a.c. commutator motors and may also be used with Schrage motors.

Dynamic braking can be applied to the synchronous motor. The supply is disconnected while the d.c. field of

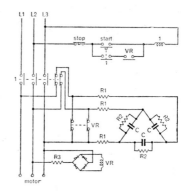

Fig. 37.—Basic connection diagram for capacitor and magnetic dynamic braking.

Operation of stop button opens supply lines and inserts capacitors *C* across motor terminals. Voltage relay *VR* provides the necessary delay before operating to short-circuit the motor terminals. Instead of VR a timer or limit switches may be used. R1 are resistors for controlling braking torque, R2 discharge resistors and R3 control resistor for relay drop-out voltage (Associated Electrical Industries Ltd.).

the motor is maintained and resistance connected across the stator winding. The machine then runs as an alternator feeding into a load of fixed resistance.

How is capacitor braking applied to induction motors?

Capacitor dynamic braking uses the ability of the induction motor to self-excite if sufficient capacitance is connected across its terminals when the supply is removed. The motor then runs as an induction generator and dissipates power with subsequent braking effect.

If the motor terminals are then short-circuited, magnetic

braking follows. A typical basic connection diagram is shown in Fig. 37. Capacitor braking followed by simultaneous magnetic and d.c.-injection braking may be applied when load inertia is very high.

5

SPEED CONTROL OF A.C. MOTORS

What 3-phase motors are available for speed control ?

In addition to the slip-ring motor, the following:

(1) Pole changing or, more recently, pole-amplitude modulated squirrel cage induction motors suitable for drives requiring two or three predetermined speeds.

(2) Induction motors with thyristor controllers to provide a variable frequency supply.

(3) Commutator motors of various types in which the rotor is supplied with a voltage of its own, allowing the speed to be varied over a wide range without energy losses.

(4) Combinations of induction motors and a.c. commutator machines, making possible any desired control of speed.

How can an induction motor be wound to give two or more speeds ?

The stator can be wound with two separate windings each with differing numbers of poles. By switching the supply lines from one to the other winding, such a stator can be made to give two different speeds. For example, 8-pole and 10-pole windings would give speeds of 750 and 600 r.p.m. (synchronous).

Another method of obtaining two speeds is to arrange a single winding, so that, by reversing one half of the coils, it can be changed to a winding having double the number of poles, for example, a 4-pole to an 8-pole winding. This

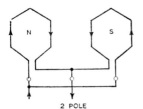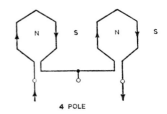

Fig. 38.—Basic arrangement of pole-change or tapped winding

is called a pole-change or tapped winding and the principle
is shown in the diagram.

Carrying the idea further, two tapped windings can be
used, resulting in a four-speed machine, for example 4/8
and 6/12 poles to give 1,500/750 r.p.m. and 1,000/500
r.p.m. (synchronous).

What is pole amplitude modulation?

This is a technique used in the design of three-phase induction motor stator windings. Using p.a.m. the motor can
be arranged to have two or more different operating speeds
with only a single stator winding. Unlike the pole-change
winding, speed ratios other than 2:1 can be obtained.
Basically, selected halves of the phase windings are reversed;
special groupings of the coil are used and in some cases
certain coils are omitted. The switching is done by control
circuitry external to the motor. A typical torque/speed
characteristic for a p.a.m. motor designed for operation at
two speeds in the ratio 1.5:1 is shown in Fig. 39.

How are p.a.m. windings connected to give two motor speeds?

Many different configurations are possible, depending on
the particular application but Fig. 40 shows a typical one.
For low speed operation the control gear connects the half
phase windings in the series-star configuration, and for high
speeds the windings are connected in parallel star.

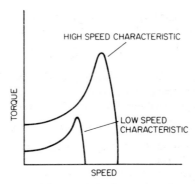

Fig. 39.—Torque-speed characteristics for two-speed p.a.m. motor with speeds in the ratio 1.5:1.

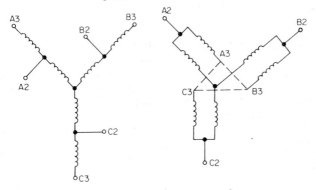

Fig. 40.—Winding arrangement for a two-speed p.a.m. motor.

For normal (unmodulated) operation:
    supply A3, B3 and C3, isolate A2, B2 and C2
For modulated operation:
    Supply A2, B2 and C2, join A3, B3 and C3

What are p.a.m. motors used for?

Applications where speed is not so critical, as in ventilation fans and some types of pumps, do not require a continuously variable speed motor with the consequent expense. Here the relative cheapness of the p.a.m. motor compared with the equivalent two-winding type is leading to the increasing use of p.a.m. motors for these applications.

What other form of speed control is used with induction motors?

Continuously variable speed can be obtained if the stator is fed with a three-phase voltage of variable frequency. Using solid-state switches known as thyristors, the frequency of the supply can be varied from zero up to about four times its original value, and this allows the speed of the motor to be varied continuously over a wide range. The thyristor therefore permits the squirrel cage induction motor to be used for variable speed applications, with the motor's attendant advantages of ruggedness, cheapness and high power to weight ratio.

What is a thyristor?

This is a three-terminal solid-state device (Fig. 41) that will conduct in one direction only (from anode to cathode)

Fig. 41.—Symbol for a thyristor—
a three-terminal solid state switch.

and then only when it is "fired" by a pulse applied to the gate terminal. When used with an a.c. supply, the thyristor will conduct, after being fired, on the positive half cycle of the supply, but when the polarity reverses it switches off by itself. When the supply goes positive a pulse must be applied to the gate of the thyristor to switch it on again. The two types of controller in most general use for controlling induction motors are the cycloconverter and the d.c. link inverter.

How does the cycloconverter work?

Fig. 42(a) shows (for simplicity) a single-phase cycloconverter (although in practice three-phase types are normally used). The waveform it produces is shown in Fig. 42(b). Different pairs of thyristors are arranged to fire (switch on) at different instants so that only parts of the

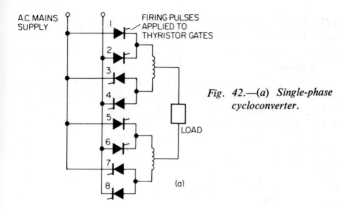

A.C. MAINS SUPPLY

FIRING PULSES APPLIED TO THYRISTOR GATES

LOAD

Fig. 42.—(a) Single-phase cycloconverter.

(a)

(b) Firing sequence and waveform produced by cycloconverter.

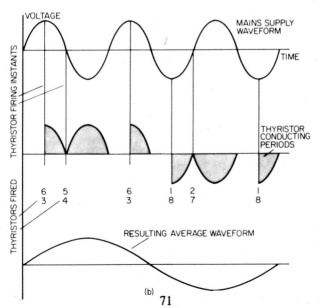

VOLTAGE

MAINS SUPPLY WAVEFORM

TIME

THYRISTOR FIRING INSTANTS

THYRISTOR CONDUCTING PERIODS

THYRISTORS FIRED

6   5
3   4

6
3

1   2
8   7

1
8

RESULTING AVERAGE WAVEFORM

(b)

71

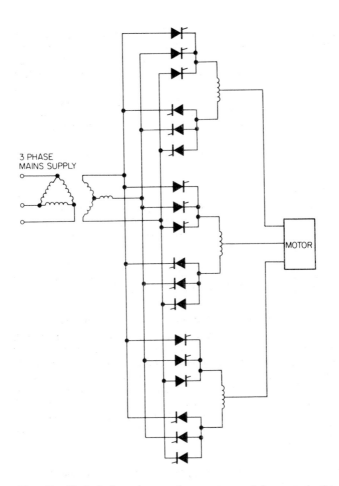

Fig. 43.—Typical three-phase cycloconverter used for control of an induction motor.

supply waveform are fed to the load. By arranging the firing instants in a certain way, the output waveform can be arranged to approximate to a low frequency sine wave. The timing of the firing is carried out in an external control unit and this can be adjusted to give a range of frequencies from zero up to about one third of the supply frequency. This allows the speed of a 2-pole motor to be varied over the range zero to 1,000 r.p.m. A complete three-phase cyclo-converter circuit is shown in Fig. 43. The interphase reactors are included to prevent the possibility of short circuiting of the supply by the thyristors.

How does the d.c. link inverter work?

The a.c. supply is rectified by a thyristor bridge and the d.c. is then converted back to a variable frequency alternating current by the thyristor inverter. This has a less restricted frequency range than the cycloconverter and can produce frequencies up to 150 Hz. This gives a speed range with a 2-pole motor of zero to 9,000 r.p.m. With small machines speeds of up to 100,000 r.p.m. are possible.

What are the disadvantages of thyristor controllers?

The main drawbacks are the cost of the thyristors and associated circuitry and the production of harmonics in the motor and the supply system. The particular disadvantage of the cycloconverter is its restricted output frequency which limits the maximum speed of any motor with which it is used. The d.c. link inverter does not suffer from this limitation as it provides a much greater range of speeds, but it involves the use of more thyristors and it is therefore more expensive.

What are the three main types of 3-phase a.c. commutator motor ?

(1) Stator-fed.
(2) Rotor-fed (or Schrage).
(3) Series.

What is the effect of supplying the rotor winding with a voltage from an external source ?

By injecting an externally-applied variable voltage, of the required frequency (through a commutator) into the rotor winding, it is possible to vary the speed of the motor above and below synchronous speed. About each of these speeds the motor behaves in the same fashion as a normal induction motor.

The principle can be explained by taking the simple example of a rotor with a standstill voltage of 100 volts induced in its windings by the rotating magnetic field with the rotor windings short-circuited. The rotor will run up to near synchronous speed if unloaded, until in fact the rotor voltage is practically zero and only sufficient current flows to supply the very small torque on no-load. If now an e.m.f. of 20 volts is supplied to the rotor in the opposite direction to, and at the same frequency as, the voltage normally induced from the rotating field, the motor will respond by running at such a speed that about 20 volts are induced in it from the field. This induced voltage will occur when the slip is 20 per cent (or the speed is 80 per cent) of the synchronous speed, and at this point the induced rotor voltage and the voltage applied to the rotor externally will practically balance.

If the 20 volts injected into the rotor winding is in the same direction as the normal induced rotor voltage, the motor will run up to 20 per cent above synchronous speed before the voltages balance, because above synchronism the rotor induced voltage reverses.

How does this method of speed variation compare in efficiency with rotor-resistance control of speed ?

It is much more efficient because the power applied to the rotor is returned to the line. Also, changes in load do not result in large fluctuations in speed.

How does a variable-speed stator-fed a.c. commutator motor operate ?

The stator winding is of the induction motor type fed from

74

the a.c. supply. The rotor winding is connected to a commutator instead of slip rings and resembles an ordinary d.c. armature. Brushes are equally-spaced around the commutator according to the number of phases. For example, a 2-pole rotor could have 3-brushes equally spaced to give three phases. The important fact to note is that the rotating field set up by the stator windings

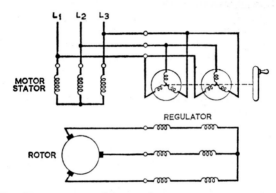

Fig. 44.—Connections for stator-fed a.c. commutator motor.

sweeps past the brushes as synchronous speed and consequently the frequency of the e.m.f. appearing at the brushes is the same as that in the stator. With a 50 Hz supply to the stator, the brush frequency will also be 50 Hz no matter at what speed the rotor is moving. Hence if we wish to supply an e.m.f. to the rotor in order to vary the speed, we can do this from a 50-Hz supply. This supply to the rotor brushes is normally obtained through an induction regulator which acts in effect like a variable-ratio transformer, enabling the injected voltage to be varied smoothly to any desired value.

The arrangement is usually called the stator-fed or fixed-brush shunt-characteristic a.c. commutator motor.

How does the variable-speed rotor-fed a.c. commutator motor work ?

In this type of motor, also called the Schrage or variable-brush a.c. commutator motor, a different method of injecting the speed-varying e.m.f. into the secondary winding is employed.

Referring to Fig. 45, the supply is led to the rotor winding through slip rings, the rotor winding being the primary.

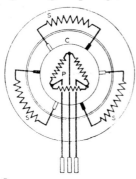

Fig. 45.—Arrangement of windings of rotor-fed (Schrage) a.c. commutator motor.

P is the primary winding, located on the rotor underneath the commutator winding and supplied through slip rings. *S* is the secondary winding located on stator. *C* is the commutator.

◻ = BRUSHES ON ONE ROCKER
◼ = BRUSHES ON THE OTHER ROCKER

The secondary winding is on the stator. On the rotor is an additional regulating winding with a commutator. The ends of the stator (secondary) windings are connected to brushes disposed on the commutator.

The first point to notice is that when the rotor is at standstill, the rotating field sweeps past the secondary winding and the brushes at synchronous speed. As the motor gains speed, the frequency in the secondary windings and, due to the commutator, the frequency at the brushes are both reduced simultaneously. No matter at what speed the rotor is moving, the brush frequency ties up with the secondary frequency and, as a result, voltage can be picked up from the commutator and injected into the secondary windings.

76

The method of varying the e.m.f. injected into the secondary windings is by altering the amount of commutator spanned by each pair of brushes. The pairs of brushes are arranged so that they can be moved simultaneously equal distances from the in-line position. When in-line, each pair of brushes rests on the same commutator segment. At this position, each secondary phase winding is short-circuited and no phase voltage is injected; consequently the speed is that of a normal induction motor. Movement of the brushes in one direction or the other increases or decreases the speed. Brush movement can be done by handwheel or by means of a small servo or pilot motor, remotely-controlled.

The general characteristics of the rotor-fed motor are the same as those of the stator-fed type.

How does the variable-speed series a.c. commutator motor work ?

A series characteristic is provided by connecting the stator and rotor in series, as shown in the diagram. The commutator on the rotor is fed from a transformer because, in general, the supply voltage is too high to allow of satisfactory commutation. It is also useful when the supply is high-tension (e.g. 3,300 volts) and constitutes one advantage of this type, since it is virtually impossible to arrange a rotor-fed motor for a high-tension supply, although the stator-fed type is somewhat easier in this respect.

Speed is controlled by brush movement, which has the effect of varying the phase agreement between the stator and rotor and thus strengthening or weakening the field.

The speed-torque characteristic is very similar to that of a d.c. series motor, with the difference that even at the highest speed setting the no-load speed rises to only about 170 per cent of the synchronous speed. Hence there is no danger from a run-away speed if the load is removed from the motor.

This type of motor is specially suited to large printing

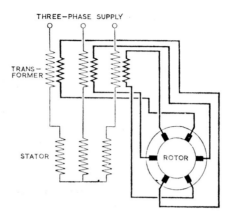

TRANS—
FORMER

STATOR

ROTOR

Fig. 46.—Typical connections of 3-phase series commutator motor.

press drives as the series characteristic gives very good load sharing amongst a group of motors driving a press.

What arrangements of control gear are required for squirrel-cage change-pole motors ?

The control gear must be selected to suit the motor windings, whether (1) a single tapped winding, (2) two separate windings, (3) two separate windings with one or both tapped.

Contactor starters are usual, although small sizes may be controlled by a single contactor in conjunction with a selector switch.

Direct-on-line starting is normal, but sometimes the contactors are interlocked so that starting must be at the lowest speed connection. This is only specified to protect the driven machine, as a change-pole motor is suitable for starting on any speed connection.

For motors with a single tapped winding giving two speeds, three contactors or switch positions are required. Two alternative winding connections commonly used are shown.

For motors having two separate windings giving two

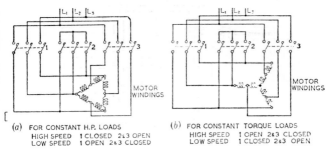

(a) FOR CONSTANT H.P. LOADS	(b) FOR CONSTANT TORQUE LOADS
HIGH SPEED 1 CLOSED 2&3 OPEN	HIGH SPEED 1 OPEN 2&3 CLOSED
LOW SPEED 1 OPEN 2&3 CLOSED	LOW SPEED 1 CLOSED 2&3 OPEN

Fig. 47.—Basic diagrams of control for two-speed change-pole a.c. motor.

speeds, two direct-on-line contactors, one for each winding, are used and are interlocked to prevent both closing together.

For motors with two separate windings, one or both tapped, a combination of the above is required.

How is the stator-fed commutator motor controlled ?

The stator-fed commutator motor has the supply taken to the stator, while a separate regulator for speed control is wired to fixed brush gear on the commutator.

Depending on the speed range, direct-on-starting may be used, with a low-speed interlock fitted on the regulator to ensure that the machine is set for starting before the circuit-breaker or supply contactor can be closed. A typical circuit is shown.

Where the speed range is short, direct-on-line starting may not be permissible and some form of resistance starting is then required. This may be either primary or secondary resistance, rotor resistance being usual on high-voltage supplies or where high torque at starting is required. The diagram shows two methods of connecting the starting resistance.

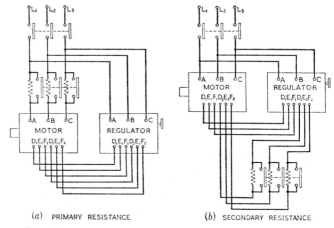

(a) PRIMARY RESISTANCE   (b) SECONDARY RESISTANCE

Fig. 48.— Resistance starting of stator-fed a.c. commutator motor.

80

6

SYNCHRONOUS MOTORS

What are 3-phase synchronous motors ?

Motors of moderate to large power in which the rotor, having been brought up to speed, is pulled into step with the rotating field and therefore runs at a constant synchronous speed. There are two main types—salient-pole synchronous and synchronous-induction. Normally both types have a similar stator winding to that of the induction motor. This winding when connected to the supply develops a rotating field, but after starting instead of using it to induce e.m.f.s in the rotor conductors, torque is obtained by introducing fixed-polarity magnetic fields on the rotor to operate in conjunction with the currents in the stator.

Generally synchronous motors are arranged to start as induction motors and, when up to full induction-motor speed, are converted to synchronous running by injecting direct current into the rotor windings. The rotor then pulls into step with the stator rotating field.

How does the rotor of a salient-pole synchronous motor operate ?

The rotor has salient-poles similar in construction to the rotor of an alternator. It usually starts as a squirrel-cage motor by means of copper bars embedded in the pole faces, the bars being connected together by end-rings to form a squirrel-cage winding. After running up to full induction-motor speed, the rotor pulls into synchronism through the action of d.c. current flowing in the rotating field coils and derived from a d.c. exciter.

Lower starting current for a given torque is obtained by employing an insulated 3-phase winding located in the pole faces, instead of using a simple squirrel-cage, the winding being connected through slip rings to an external resistance. The resistance is varied during the starting period as for a slip-ring induction motor.

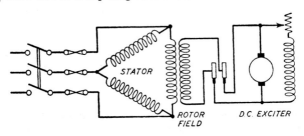

Fig. 49.—Three-phase synchronous motor.

How is the rotor of a synchronous induction motor constructed ?

The rotor closely resembles that of a slip-ring induction motor and is run up by means of a rotor-resistance starter in the same way as a slip-ring induction motor. Low-voltage synchronous-induction motors may be of "inverted" construction, with the primary windings on the rotor and the secondary on the stator.

What are the applications of synchronous motors ?

The d.c. excitation of the rotor can be increased to a point where it takes over the magnetising function of the stator. In this event, the stator power factor is increased to unity, so that no wattless lagging current flows from the supply to the motor. By increasing the excitation current beyond this point, the stator current can be made leading and this leading current can be used to magnetise any other motors connected to the supply in the factory, thus further improving the overall power factor of the system. The synchronous motor therefore serves the dual purpose of providing a constant-speed drive for a large piece of machinery that requires to be run continuously and at the same time of operating at unity power factor or any desired leading power factor, in order to correct the low power factor in the remainder of the plant.

Synchronous motors are normally suitable for only one specified direction of rotation.

The synchronous-induction motor gives a better starting performance, but the salient-pole type with squirrel-cage is preferred, when starting performance permits, because it gives about $1\frac{1}{2}$ per cent higher efficiency.

What control gear is required for synchronous motors ?

The d.c.-excitation equipment comprises the field switch with discharge resistance and the exciter-field rheostat.

The a.c. equipment will depend on the type of starting used.

If started as a squirrel-cage induction motor, the damping winding in the pole faces act as the induction-motor secondary, while the field windings are usually connected to the discharge resistance.

Direct-on-line, auto-transformer or primary resistance or reactor starting is usual, depending on the starting current permitted or on the torque required.

The motor accelerates to a speed just below synchronism, whereupon the excitation circuit is completed and the machine pulls into step as the field builds up.

A power-factor meter is usually included so that after synchronising, the excitation can be adjusted to give the required power factor.

Automatic installations involving starting, synchronising and possibly power-factor control are available. The majority of synchronous-motor equipments, however, comprise individual units, such as stator oil-switch, auto-transformer or reactor with associated switches if required for starting, and an excitation panel including power-factor meter and ammeter.

If the machine is started as a slip-ring motor, a secondary winding in the rotor-pole faces may be connected to slip rings; alternatively, the exciting winding may be of the distributed type which also serves as a motor winding for starting purposes. In the first type, the slip-ring winding remains short-circuited after starting and acts as a pole-face damper. With the distributed dual-purpose winding, provision is made in the control gear for connecting it to the exciter for synchronising.

What is a reluctance motor?

This is a special form of synchronous motor that does not require excitation of the rotor. A rotating field is produced by the stator normally by a three-phase winding although single-phase types are available. The important feature of the reluctance motor is that there are two flux paths through the rotor, called the direct axis and the quadrature axis. These two paths have very different reluctances and the reluctance torque arises from the tendency of the rotor to align itself in the minimum reluctance position relative to the rotating magnetic field. The reluctance torque is maintained only at synchronous speed and so a cage winding is incorporated for starting purposes.

What are the applications of reluctance motors?

Reluctance motors are used in synchronised multi-motor drives, for operation of rotating stores in computers, and nuclear rod positioning drives.

7

SINGLE-PHASE MOTORS

When are single-phase motors employed ?

When the only available alternating-current supply is single-phase. In general, when a 3-phase supply is available, 3-phase motors are preferred, although exceptions are often made in the case of fractional-kilowatt drives.

What types of single-phase motors are in use ?

(1) Induction motors (split-phase, capacitor and shaded-pole).
(2) Repulsion and repulsion-induction motors.
(3) Universal motors.
(4) Unexcited synchronous motors.

What is the principle of the single-phase induction motor ?

A single-phase winding sets up an alternating magnetic field. Since this field does not rotate a single-phase winding alone cannot produce torque to start the motor from rest. Once the motor has been started, however, it will continue to run provided the load is not too high. To start the motor electrically, it is necessary to employ an auxiliary winding in parallel and make the current in this winding differ in phase from the current in the main winding. Simulating a 2-phase supply in this way, the combined effect of the fields set up by the two windings is a more or less effective rotating field, thus providing a starting torque.

After starting, rotation of the field is carried out by

currents set up in the secondary winding and the auxiliary primary winding is generally switched out of circuit.

How does the single-phase split-phase induction motor work ?

The auxiliary winding is usually wound with about the same number of turns as the main winding but of much smaller wire. Because of the higher resistance of the auxiliary winding, the current in it is more in phase with

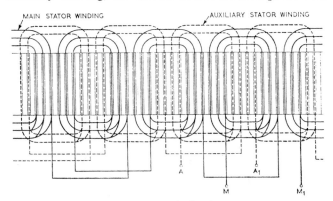

MAIN STATOR WINDING   AUXILIARY STATOR WINDING

Fig. 50.—Windings of split-phase motor.

the supply voltage than is the current in the main winding. In practice, a phase difference of about 30° is attained, which is somewhat lower than the ideal value of 90° but sufficient to give ample starting torque against light load.

The auxiliary winding is usually short-time rated—it would overheat if left in circuit for more than a few seconds—so it is cut out of circuit immediately starting is accomplished.

What are the applications of the split-phase induction motor ?

Fractional-kilowatt drives for appliances that can be

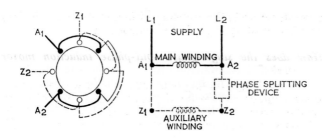

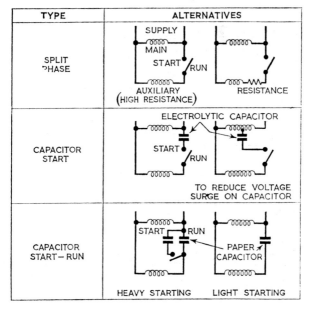

Fig. 51.—Typical single-phase-motor starting connections.

Capacitor start-run motors give superior running characteristics, high power factor and silent operation.

87

brought up to speed quickly. A typical starting torque is 175 to 200 per cent of the full-load torque.

What is a capacitor motor ?

A single-phase induction motor in which the difference in phase between the main and auxiliary windings is effected by connecting a capacitor in series with the auxiliary winding. Because of the capacitor, the auxiliary-phase current approaches 90° in advance of the main-phase current, giving a much higher starting torque than is possible with a split-phase motor.

There are three main types of capacitor motor:

(1) Capacitor-start induction-run (the capacitor winding being in circuit only during the starting period).

(2) Permanent split-capacitor motor, in which the capacitor winding is in circuit for both starting and running.

(3) Capacitor start-and-run motor, using two capacitors for starting, one of them being cut out for running.

When is the capacitor-start motor used ?

When really high starting torque is necessary, as for example motors driving refrigerator compressors. A starting torque of 300 per cent or more can be obtained.

What type of capacitor is employed for capacitor-start motors ?

Generally a dry-type electrolytic capacitor because it has large value of capacitance in small bulk and is the cheapest. This type of capacitor is short-time rated for a.c. working and is therefore suitable only for starting applications where the duty is intermittent.

As the voltage across starting capacitors can be higher than the mains voltage, their voltage rating must be suitable, for example, 275 volt rating for 200-250-volt motors, when the capacitor is connected in the usual way in series with the auxiliary winding. Fig. 52 shows a method of connecting a capacitor to allow its working-voltage rating to be lower than mains voltage.

What are the applications of the permanent split-capacitor motor?

For small motors with light starting duties, such as fan drives and oil burners. Only a small capacitor is required and this is left in circuit to avoid the complication of the extra switch. The fact that the auxiliary winding is in circuit whilst running improves the machine performance

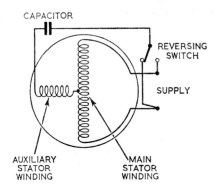

Fig. 52.—Capacitor-motor tee connection.
The diagram also shows connections for a reversing switch.

considerably in respect of power factor and quiet running. A paper-dielectric capacitor must be used, because the electrolytic capacitor is not suitable for continuous operation.

What is the object of using two capacitors?

A capacitor-start capacitor-run motor can be employed when the starting duty is severe and it is desired to achieve a high power-factor when running. A smaller capacitance is required for running than for starting, so two capacitors are used in parallel for starting and one capacitor is cut out for running. Special care in the design is necessary when capacitors are run in parallel, as a high surge voltage can take place on switching out.

When are slip-ring single-phase motors used ?

With larger single-phase induction motors it is usual practice to have slip-ring rotors giving a higher starting efficiency in terms of torque per ampere. The rotor winding and starting resistances are standard 3-phase components.

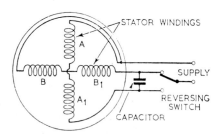

Fig. 53.—*Connections for high-torque reversible capacitor motor.*

How is the single-phase induction motor switched from start to run ?

Switching is usually done automatically by a centrifugal switch mounted on the motor shaft, but it can also be done by hand switching by responsible operators.

An alternative to the use of a centrifugal switch is a specially-designed relay switch or contactor switch which controls the starting winding.

What types of relay are used for starting single-phase induction motors?

Three common types are (a) Current relay (b) Potential relay (c) Positive temperature coefficient relay (P.T.C.).

How does the current relay operate ?

The relay is normally open and has a coil of heavy wire connected in series with the "run" winding. When the motor is switched on the surge of current closes the relay contacts to connect the supply to the "start" winding. As the motor accelerates the current in the "run" winding quickly falls and the relay drops out, generally by gravity, to disconnect the "start" winding.

How does the potential relay operate ?

The relay is normally closed and has a coil of fine wire connected in parallel with the "start" winding. As the motor speeds up the voltage across the "start" winding opens the relay and disconnects the "start" winding from the supply. The induced voltage across the "start" winding when the motor is running keeps the relay open.

How does the P.T.C. relay operate ?

A disc of semiconductor material in series with the "start" winding conducts the current to the "start" winding. The current taken by this winding quickly warms the semiconductor disc causing it to have a high resistance so that only a very small current now flows through the circuit but sufficient to maintain the temperature of the disc in its resistive state.

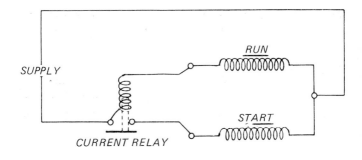

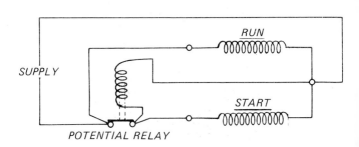

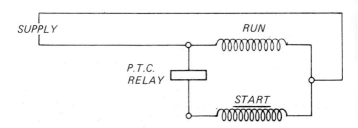

Fig. 54(a).—Single-phase starting relay types

How is a split-phase or capacitor induction motor reversed?

By changing over the ends of the starting winding at the motor.

What is a shaded-pole motor ?

A type of single-phase induction motor for very small powers in which a starting torque is provided by permanently short-circuited coils displaced in position from

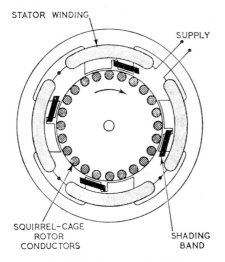

Fig. 54(b).—Shaded-pole motor

the main stator coils. The rotor is squirrel-cage. The most usual form of a motor of this type has salient poles on the stator somewhat similar to the poles of a universal motor. Each pole is unequally divided by a slot cut in the laminations allowing one side of the pole to be surrounded by a heavy copper band, known as a shading coil or loop.

Other forms of shaded-pole motor have the normal induction motor stator, its windings consisting of single-phase winding and a shading winding, the latter being wave-wound and short-circuited inside the motor or at its terminals.

How does the shaded-pole motor operate ?

The e.m.f. induced in the shading coil will always be such as to oppose the change which causes it (Lenz's Law). It therefore resists and delays the build-up or collapse of the magnetic field in the shaded portion of the pole, resulting in a sweeping magnetic field across the pole face towards the shading coil.

What are the applications of the shaded-pole motor ?

This type of motor requires no automatic centrifugal or other type of starting switch since there is no starting winding to be switched out of circuit. Its simple construction makes it a particularly robust machine suitable for long-hour duty. It is not, however, as efficient electrically as other single-phase induction motors mainly on account of the fairly-heavy copper-losses in the pole-shading loops. Usual sizes of such motors are up to about 25 W and they are used where efficiency is of little importance, such as for driving small fans, motorised valves, recording instruments, record players, etc.

Can the shaded-pole motor be reversed ?

The motor is normally not reversible since this would involve mechanical dismantling and reassembly. Special machines are made comprising two rotors on a common shaft, each having its own stator assembled for opposite directions of rotation.

What is a universal motor ?

A motor in the fractional kilowatt range of about 10 to 400 W constructed on similar lines to a series-type d.c. motor adapted to a.c. by having a completely-laminated field core. They cannot satisfactorily be made to run at less than about 2,000 r.p.m.

If similar performance on a.c. and d.c. is required from motors running at less than about 3,000 r.p.m., a tapped field winding is desirable.

How are universal motors started ?

By switching straight on to the line. Starting torques of up to about five-times full-load torque with starting currents of about three to four times full-load current, depending upon the size and speed of the motor, are usual.

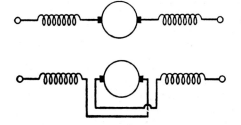

Fig. 55.—Reversal of universal motor.

The connections to the armature windings are changed over to reverse the motor.

What are the applications of universal motors ?

Universal motors have a series characteristic so that they run at their rated speed only on the rated load. If the load is reduced the speed will rise. Such motors are suitable for driving fans, vacuum cleaners, domestic sewing machines, portable tools, etc. where the load is constant, or where a steadily-maintained speed is not important. As brush wear takes place more rapidly in universal motors they are not generally considered suitable for long-hour duty. Speed control and reversing can be arranged as for d.c. motors. Three-lead reversing, which greatly simplifies the control gear, can be arranged, two separate fields being provided, one for each direction of rotation.

What are repulsion motors?

Single-phase machines made up to about 4 kW having a stator wound with a single-phase winding and a rotor very similar to a d.c. armature with commutator. The brushes are permanently short-circuited. Currents induced in the rotor by the magnetic field from the stator give the rotor a magnetic polarity that, with suitable brush position on the commutator, causes repulsion to take place between like poles of the stator and rotor. No rotation results if the brush axis corresponds with the axis of the stator winding, called the neutral position, the magnetic polarity of the rotor then being the same as that of the stator.

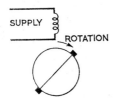

Fig. 56.—Repulsion-motor connections

The stator is wound with a single-phase winding. The rotor is very similar to a d.c. motor armature with commutator.

In this form, the machine is a plain repulsion motor having series characteristics, with which speed rises as the load on the motor is reduced.

The machine is often converted into an induction motor during the period of running by arranging that all the commutator segments are short-circuited by a centrifugally-operated device when the motor is up to speed. The brushes are also lifted in some cases to reduce wear.

To avoid the complication of the short-circuiting device, the rotor may be arranged with a squirrel-cage winding at the bottom of the slots. This takes over at speed and gives induction-motor characteristics.

How are repulsion motors reversed?

To get reversed rotation, the brushes are moved round to a corresponding point on the other side of the neutral position. When it is desired to avoid having to move the

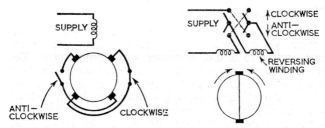

Fig. 57.—Two methods of reversing repulsion-motor direction of rotation by switching.

brushes, two sets of brushes may be used, one set for each rotation and to short-circuit them as required. Another method of avoiding brush movement is by tapping the stator winding and changing the direction of rotation by shifting the axis of the stator poles. This is usually done by one reversing winding in addition to the main winding and a change-over switch, as shown in the diagram.

What are the applications of repulsion motors ?

The repulsion motor is suitable for drives requiring very high starting torques, although it has been replaced to a large extent by the capacitor motor.

Where variable speed is required, a plain repulsion motor (without the short-circuiting and brush-lifting mechanism) can be used, the speed control being obtainable by rocking the brushes which may be connected to a hand-wheel or lever on the motor end-bracket.

8

DIRECT-CURRENT MOTORS

What are the two basic types of d.c. motor ?

The shunt motor and the series motor. In the shunt motor, the field and armature windings are connected in parallel across the supply. In the series motor, both these windings are connected in series with the supply.

The combination of shunt and series field windings result in a compound-wound motor.

Why is a commutator essential in a d.c. motor ?

To reverse the currents in the armature coils as they pass from one pole system to the next so as to obtain a

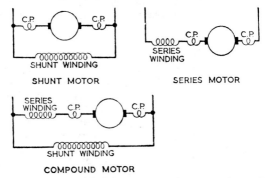

Fig. 58.—Connections of shunt, series and compound-wound motors

C.P., commutating poles, or interpoles, are not fitted on the smallest motors.

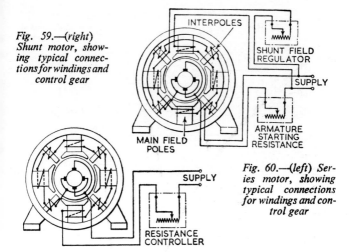

Fig. 59.—(right) Shunt motor, showing typical connections for windings and control gear

INTERPOLES

SHUNT FIELD REGULATOR

SUPPLY

ARMATURE STARTING RESISTANCE

MAIN FIELD POLES

SUPPLY

Fig. 60.—(left) Series motor, showing typical connections for windings and control gear

RESISTANCE CONTROLLER

steady forward torque. If direct current were to be passed into the armature windings through slip rings, the result would be that after rotation through a pole pitch, the current, being in the same direction, would develop a torque in the reverse rotation and no continuous motion would be obtainable.

On what does the speed of a d.c. motor depend ?

The speed at which the armature revolves depends on the number of armature conductors in series and the total magnetic flux of all the poles in the machine. When the line voltage is applied to the armature, certain voltage drops occur due to the passage of the current through the brushes into the commutator, together with further voltage drops due to the circulation of the current around the armature coils. Finally, with stable conditions, the armature must rotate in its magnetic field at such a speed that a back-voltage is generated equal to the applied line voltage, less the voltage drops already mentioned.

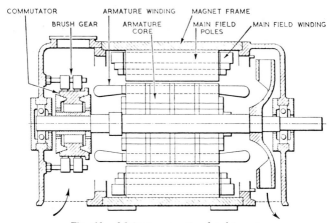

COMMUTATOR   ARMATURE WINDING   MAGNET FRAME

BRUSH GEAR   ARMATURE CORE   MAIN FIELD POLES   MAIN FIELD WINDING

Fig. 61.—Main components of a d.c. motor

What are the basic components in d.c. motor construction?

(1) The magnet frame, of cast steel or fabricated from mild-steel plate.

(2) Main field poles. Since the magnetic poles are stationary in space, only one coil is used per pole and each main field pole consists of laminations of electrical sheet steel riveted together. For large machines, the pole tips only may be laminated.

(3) Interpoles of mild steel, with their windings, are employed on all d.c. motors except the smallest.

(4) Laminated armature core built up on the shaft or rotor hub, with the windings distributed in slots equally spaced around the periphery of the armature.

(5) A commutator built up from thin segments of copper with strips of micanite to insulate the segments from each other. A moulded construction may be employed in very small motors.

(6) Brushes of carbon-copper composition supported in brush boxes and spring loaded.

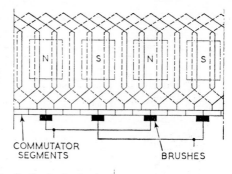

Fig. 62.—(right)
Simple 4-pole 12-slot lap armature winding

Two-layer winding, the lower coil sides being indicated by dotted lines.

COMMUTATOR SEGMENTS

BRUSHES

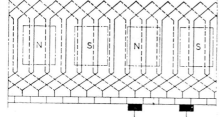

Fig. 63.—(left)
Simple 4-pole 13-slot two-layer wave armature winding

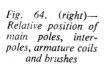

INTERPOLES

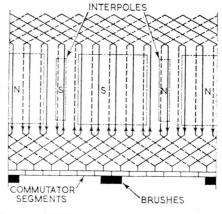

Fig. 64. (right)—
Relative position of main poles, interpoles, armature coils and brushes

The polarity of the interpoles is the same as that of the preceding main pole.

COMMUTATOR SEGMENTS

BRUSHES

101

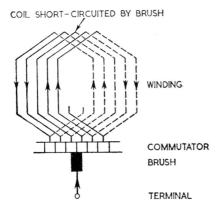

COIL SHORT-CIRCUITED BY BRUSH

WINDING

COMMUTATOR

BRUSH

TERMINAL

Fig. 65.—Armature coil undergoing commutation

Why are interpoles used ?

Interpoles are fitted between the main poles except in the very smallest machines. As an armature coil passes through the space between the main poles, it undergoes commutation—the two ends of the coil are short-circuited by the brush before current is reversed in the coil. The dying away of the magnetic flux surrounding the coil conductors and its rise in the opposite direction causes a self-induced voltage in the coil which delays current reversal. This delay leads to bad commutation, indicated by sparking at the trailing edge of the brushes. Poor commutation can be reduced to some extent by moving the brushes from the geometric neutral position backwards relative to the direction of rotation and by using brushes having a higher contact resistance. The delay in current reversal can be corrected by inducing into the shorted coils a voltage in opposition to the self-induced voltage. This is the function of the interpoles.

How are interpole windings connected ?

In series with the armature windings and with a polarity of interpole opposite to that of the main pole following the interpole in the direction of rotation (i.e. the interpole has the same polarity as the preceding main pole against the direction of rotation).

9

CONTROL GEAR FOR D.C. MOTORS

Why is it necessary to have special starting gear for d.c. motors ?

Because of their low armature resistance, d.c. motors except in the smallest sizes are unsuitable for connecting direct to the supply. At starting, the voltage across the armature must be limited to a value that gives a safe and satisfactory starting current.

Are there any cases where d.c. motors may be started by switching directly on to the supply ?

Yes. Series or compound-wound motors up to about 500 W and shunt-wound motors up to about 200 W. All motors of 400 W and above should have under-voltage and overload protection.

What is the usual method of starting ?

To connect in series with the armature a resistor that is short-circuited, generally in steps, as the motor accelerates. Switching may be by hand-operation or automatic.

Show how speed, torque and current vary when starting a d.c. motor

Fig. 66 shows the speed/torque curve for the various steps of a typical starter and Fig. 67 a typical time/current relationship. When the line switch is closed, armature current I_1 flows, producing the starting torque T_1. The motor accelerates and the back e.m.f. it produces gradually reduces the armature current to I_2 and the motor torque to T_2, the load torque, here taken as full-load value. To maintain acceleration when the falling current approaches

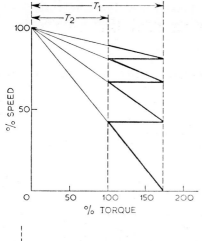

Fig. 66.—*Speed/torque curve for the various steps of a d.c. shunt-motor starter*

T_1, starting torque.
T_2, load torque.

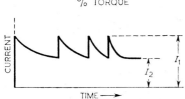

Fig. 67.—*Current/time curve for the various steps of a d.c. shunt-motor starter*

I_2, the first step of resistance is switched out, reducing the value of the starting resistor, which is so graded that the armature current and motor torque rise to their original values of I_1 and T_1 producing further acceleration. Short-circuiting of the starting resistor is repeated step-by-step, as shown in the curve until the motor is connected direct to the supply. It then accelerates along its characteristic speed/torque curve to normal working speed.

105

What is the simplest form of starter for a d.c. motor ?

The hand-operated faceplate starter. Its application is generally confined to low power motors because its switch is not suitable for breaking large currents. Six or more starting-resistance steps are usual. When frequent starting or inching is required, it is desirable to employ a starter specially-designed for making and breaking current—a specially robust faceplate starter in which all the current-

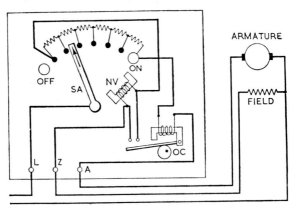

Fig. 68.—Connection diagram of a faceplate starter for a shunt motor
NV, under-voltage or no-volt coil. OC, overload coil. SA, starter arm.

breaking takes place at a single-pole contactor fitted with arc-shield and magnetic blow-out, or a hand-operated drum-type starter, or the use of electromagnetic contactors.

How is a faceplate starter operated ?

First ensure that the starter-switch lever is in the "off" position. Then close the main switch and move the handle slowly towards the full-on position. The acceleration of the motor and the associated current and torque peaks are dependent upon the operator. To limit current peaks to a minimum while starting, sufficient time must be allowed on each step of the starter for the motor to reach the maximum possible speed.

The motor should always be stopped by switching off at the main switch and not by knocking the switch lever to the off position, a procedure likely to result in burnt and sticking contacts and failure subsequently to release automatically on overload.

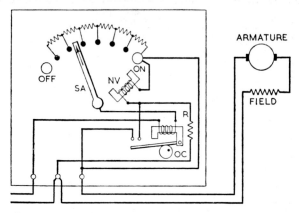

Fig. 69.—Connection diagram of a faceplate starter for a series motor

How is under-voltage and overload protection provided on faceplate starters ?

In the simple faceplate starter, undervoltage protection often comprises an electromagnet holding the starter arm in the full-on position. Any voltage failure or fall of voltage to an undersirable low value (or an open-circuit in the shunt-field windings of a shunt-field motor) causes the starter arm, which is spring-loaded, to return to the "off" position by the action of the spring.

For overload protection, simple faceplate starters have an overload electromagnet connected in series with the armature winding. If the motor is overloaded, the armature

107

of the overload magnet is attracted so that its contacts short-circuit the under-voltage coil and trip the starter.

When a contactor is used to make and break the main circuit, overload release can be obtained through an overload relay controlling the contactor-coil circuit.

Further operating protection can be obtained with a contactor, since it can be arranged to interlock with the starting handle so that the contactor will only close with the starting handle in the "start" position and will only remain closed if the handle is left in the full-on position. No special provision has to be made with a contactor to obtain under voltage release.

What is a drum-type starter ?

A hand-operated starter or controller used in preference to a faceplate starter when the starting is arduous and frequent. The design allows fixed and moving contacts of robust construction and enables each fixed contact or finger to be independently held against the drum by a separate spring. When a contactor is incorporated, the starter can be designed for the starting of very large motors. The drum starter unit is often restricted to short-circuiting the starting resistor, the contactor making and interrupting the motor current.

What is a contactor starter ?

A type of starter in which supply line make-and-break and the closing of successive accelerating contacts, short-circuiting steps of starting resistance, are performed by magnetically-operated contactors or relays. The diagram shows the basic connections for a shunt-motor contactor starter. Pushing the "start" button energises the contactor coil or coils 1L and 2L, closing the line switches (1L and 2L). Armature current flows through the starting resistance producing the starting torque. At the same time, the auxiliary contacts 1L and 2L close, energising the next contactor in sequence (1A), but a period elapses before it closes its contacts. The motor accelerates and when the contacts 1A close, the first step of resistance is short-circuited. The contactor coil 2A is energised through the closing of the auxiliary contact 1A. The contacts 2A will not close immediately because of the delay feature. The remaining steps of resistance are successively shorted out in the same manner in due course by contacts 2A and 3A.

How is the delay period between the closing of successive accelerating contacts obtained ?

A variety of methods are used for ensuring the correct intervals between the closing of accelerating contacts or

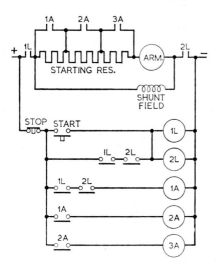

Fig. 70.—Basic diagram of a contactor starter for a shunt-motor application suitable for fast acceleration (without a separate timing device)

1A, 2A and 3A are accelerating contactors, their inherent time lag in operation being used to control the rate of acceleration.

contactors. These methods fall into two groups: time control and current control.

How is time control of acceleration effected ?

By employing some form of timing relay to obtain a preset-time delay between the closing of successive acceler-

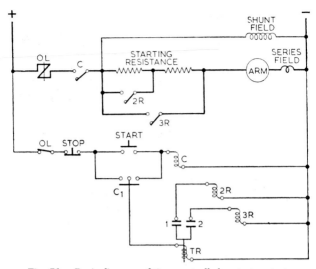

Fig. 71.—Basic diagram of time-controlled contactor starter

Closure of the start pushbutton operates the main contactor C. This connects the motor to the supply in series with the starter resistor, closes auxiliary contacts C1 and energises the coil of the timing relay TR. Contacts 1 and 2 of TR close successively at time intervals determined by the setting of TR, thus operating the corresponding accelerating contactors 2R and 3R.

ating contacts or contactors, the interval being independent of the load on the motor. For drives where extremely-fast acceleration is required, the time it takes for contactors to close after becoming energised may be utilised as the timing element, no separate timing device being required (see Fig. 70).

Accelerating contactors may not be used in small starters; instead, staggered fingers acting as accelerating contacts are operated in succession by the action of a solenoid-operated timing relay or other means, the timing between the closing of successive fingers being determined, for example, by an adjustable oil dashpot.

For larger powers, the timing-relay-operated accelerating

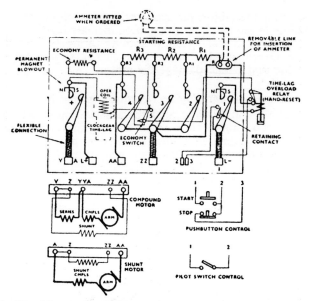

Fig. 72.—Diagram of connections of constant-time contactor starter for motors up to 15 kW

On pressing the start button or closing the pilot switch, the contactor operating coil is energised. The accelerating contacts 2, 3 and 4 cut out steps of starting resistance. The rate at which the accelerating contacts close is governed by a clockwork mechanism. The two main contacts, which deal with the line current, are fitted with permanent-magnet blow-outs.

contacts, closing successively, energise the operating coils of accelerating contactors.

Many different forms of timing relay are in use, usually adjustable so that the closing of the accelerating contacts or contactors can match normal-load requirements, giving smooth acceleration.

How does time-control react to abnormal load when starting ?

Should the initial starting torque be insufficient to

111

accelerate the motor, the accelerating contactors continue to close in sequence, resulting in an increased current and torque, and increasing the possibility of accelerating the drive. Overload relays prevent the current from reaching a value that would damage the motor.

How is current control of acceleration obtained ?

Figs. 66 and 67 show that the accelerating contactors or contacts should close when the starting current has fallen to its minimum value. Under current control, the accelerating contactors are prevented from closing until the current is actually reduced to this figure. Thus, the interval between the closing of successive accelerating contactors is the time taken for the starting current to drop from maximum to minimum, which depends upon

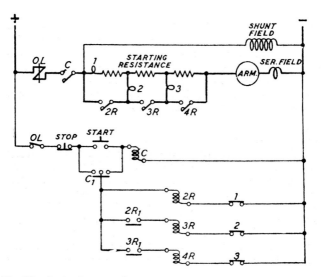

Fig. 73.—Basic diagram of current-controlled starter, series-relay type

the motor loading. The accelerating contactors are usually mechanically or electrically held open by relays carrying the motor current or some fraction of it.

The illustration shows a typical basic diagram of this type of starter. When the motor is first switched on to the supply, the resulting rush of current through the first series-relay coil (1) opens its contacts (1) (before accelerating contactor 2R has had time to operate). As the motor accelerates and its current falls, the first series relay (1) operates to close the operating-coil circuit of the first accelerating contactor (2R). When this contactor closes, the second series relay (2) behaves in a similar manner to the first; in closing its contacts (2), it energises the operating-coil of the second accelerating contactor (3R). The process is repeated until the motor has been automatically accelerated to full speed.

Why is it essential that current control be arranged to accelerate the maximum load likely to be applied ?

Should the motor fail to accelerate due to insufficient starting torque, the sustained starting current will prevent the accelerating contactors from closing and, unless the starter is disconnected, damage may result to the motor or to a short-time-rated starting resistor.

What is series lock-out control of acceleration ?

A method of current control in which each accelerating contactor is fitted with an additional coil, termed the series lock-out or hold-off coil. All the series coils are in series with the starting resistance. The magnetic pull exerted by the series coil acts in opposition to the pull of the contactor shunt-closing coil. The iron circuit of the lock-out is so adjusted that the pull of the coil, when carrying starting current above the minimum, overcomes the pull of the contactor closing coil and holds the contactor open.

An alternative method is to employ shunt hold-out

coils, each coil being connected across a section of the starting resistance and operating on voltage drop.

What is counter-e.m.f. control of automatic acceleration ?

Another method of control used on light-starting duty where only one or two starting steps are required. It makes use of the fact that the voltage or back-e.m.f. across the armature increases in proportion to the speed as the motor accelerates. The operating coil of the accelerating contactor is connected across the armature and operates its contactor at a predetermined voltage below that of the

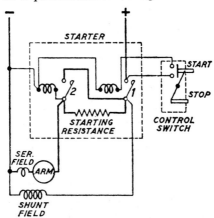

Fig. 74.—Connections of a counter-e.m.f. starter

supply. When the motor is connected to the supply at starting, the voltage across the accelerating-contactor coil increases gradually until a value is reached sufficient to close this contactor and thus short-circuit a step of starting resistance.

An alternative arrangement is to connect adjustable voltage relays across the armature, their operation closing the accelerating contactors, the coils of which remain on full supply voltage.

How is the starting period with current control affected by the motor loading ?

The total duration of the starting time is proportional to the load on the motor. This feature is of value in cases where it is required that the motor should always accelerate in the minimum time consistent with the load conditions and that heavy loads be accelerated more slowly than light ones.

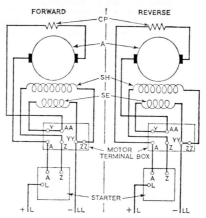

Fig. 75.—Reversing a compound-wound d.c. motor

Showing reversal by changing over the armature and interpole connections A and AA in the motor-terminal box.   If the motor sparks, adjust the brush position.

How is reversal of a d.c. motor obtained ?

By changing the direction of the current through either the armature or the field. Usually reversal of the current through the armature is adopted. If *both* armature and field connections are reversed the motor will run in the original direction.

When reversing the armature connections, treat the interpole coils as part of the armature winding.

If reversal of rotation is made by changing the field

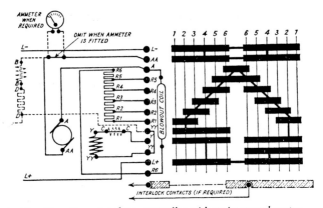

Fig. 76.—Reversing-drum controller with series-wound motor

Connections for either a shunt or series brake-solenoid are shown by B-B-D-D or C-C. On d.c. circuits the controller is fitted with a magnetic blow-out coil to reduce arcing. Fig. 77 shows connections for series limit switches.

If, when a protective panel is used together with a shunt-wound brake solenoid, it is desired to apply the brake when the main contactor opens, the solenoid connection D-YY should be omitted and replaced by a connection to L+ through an auxiliary contactor or contacts that open when the main contactor is tripped.

Limit switches if used should be double-pole, the extra pole being used for the shunt-solenoid circuit.

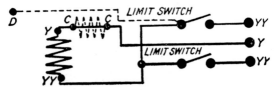

Fig. 77.—Connections for series limit switches with reversing drum controller circuit of Fig. 76

connections, change both shunt- and series-field connections on a compound-wound motor.

What is a field-failure relay ?

A protective device that opens a shunt-motor starter

116

should the motor field collapse. Its application is usually restricted to drives where loss of the field would result in a dangerous condition such as overspeeding or the loss of dynamic braking. The operating coil of the relay is connected in series with the field whilst its normally-open trip contacts are in the under-voltage release circuit.

How can the speed of a d.c. motor be increased ?

With shunt motors a speed-range above rated speed can be obtained by field weakening that is by connecting resistance in series with the shunt-field circuit.

Why should weakening the field result in speed increase ?

A back-e.m.f. is always induced in the armature coils as they rotate through the field flux and is always equal to the applied voltage, less any voltage drop in armature

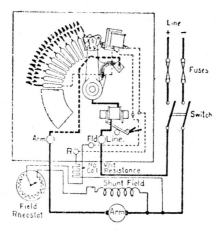

Fig. 78.—Faceplate starter for variable-speed shunt or compound-wound motor

With series-connected shunt-field rheostat and separately-excited under-voltage (no-volt) coil. This starter has a laminated short-circuiting brush.

resistance. Thus, with less field flux the motor automatically responds by speeding up in order to maintain its e.m.f.

How is a field regulator for speed control connected ?

The starter incorporates the shunt-field regulator.

When operated, this introduces one by one a number of small resistors into the field circuit. The regulator may be hand-operated or pilot-motor operated. When a large speed increase is required, the no-volt coil is connected in series with a large resistance across the supply instead of in the field circuit. This obviates the possibility of the

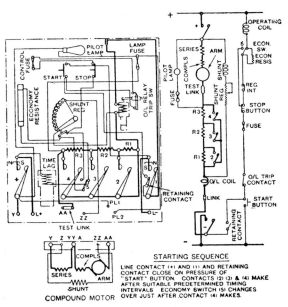

STARTING SEQUENCE

LINE CONTACT (+) AND (1) AND RETAINING
CONTACT CLOSE ON PRESSURE OF
"START" BUTTON. CONTACTS (2) (3) & (4) MAKE
AFTER SUITABLE PREDETERMINED TIMING
INTERVALS ECONOMY SWITCH (5) CHANGES
OVER JUST AFTER CONTACT (4) MAKES.

Fig. 79.—Wiring and line diagrams of constant-time contactor-starting panel, including shunt-speed regulator

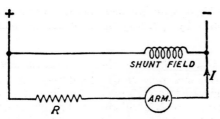

Fig. 80.—Speed reduction of shunt motor by resistance inserted in the armature circuit

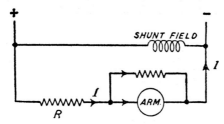

Fig. 81.—Speed reduction by shunting armature circuit

no-volt release operating due to the reduction in field current.

In order to obtain maximum-starting torque, it is essential to return the regulator to the full-field position before starting. To ensure this, some form of interlock may be fitted between the starter and the field regulator.

In cases where it is considered undesirable to disturb the setting of the field regulator when the motor is shut down, a shunt-field accelerating relay can be employed, the closing of which short circuits the regulator during acceleration to normal speed. The relay is then made to open, introducing the pre-set regulator into the field circuit, the motor accelerating to the selected speed. When the regulator is introduced, the weakening of the field is accompanied by an increase in armature current; to limit the armature current to a suitable value, the accelerating

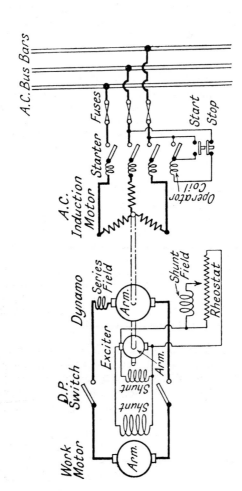

Fig. 82.—Ward-Leonard control

120

relay may be operated by a series coil connected in the armature circuit. The relay, which has a close differential, may operate several times between the normal and the higher selected speed.

How can the speed of a d.c. motor be reduced ?

Speed reduction below rated speed can be obtained by reducing the armature voltage. This may be done by connecting a rheostat in series with the motor armature, sometimes also with an armature-shunt resistance, or divertor, in order to obtain stable running when low speeds are necessary.

What is the Ward Leonard system ?

A form of speed control applied to a shunt motor that provides variable armature voltage without the waste of energy involved when armature-circuit resistors are used. The armature of the motor is supplied from its own generator, which may be driven by an a.c. motor. The field of the shunt motor is energised from a d.c. and some-times a constant source. To vary the motor armature voltage, the voltage of the generator is varied by con-trolling its field current. This can be done directly by a rheostat in the generator-field circuit or by automatic control.

Wide and accurate speed control can be obtained and reversal of the motor is effected simply by reversing the generator field. The Ward Leonard system is now being replaced by thyristor controllers for machines up to about 500 kW.

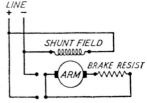

Fig. 83.—Dynamic braking of shunt-motor

Armature disconnected from the supply and connected across a resistance, the shunt field remaining energised.

How are thyristors used to control d.c. motors?

Thyristors are used to rectify the a.c. supply and, by varying the instant at which they are fired, a d.c. voltage that can be adjusted is fed to the armature. In this way the speed of the motor can be controlled. Separately excited motors are normally used with thyristor control and a three-phase fully controlled thyristor bridge is shown in Fig. 84. The field windings are energised from a separate rectifier.

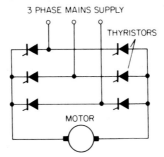

Fig. 84.—*Three-phase fully controlled thyristor bridge.*

What sort of controller is used for larger motors?

For motors above about 1 MW, a more sophisticated circuit is needed to reduce the harmonics that are produced. Fig. 85 shows a 12-pulse unit that produces a small amplitude ripple at 600 Hz.

How is counter-current braking (plugging) applied to d.c. motors ?

It is usual to keep the field connected and to reverse the supply to the armature. Since the back e.m.f. in the armature then boosts the applied voltage, additional resistance besides the starting resistance is needed in the armature circuit to limit the current to a value that can be commutated satisfactorily. This value is usually about $1\frac{1}{2}$ times the full-load current and the additional plugging

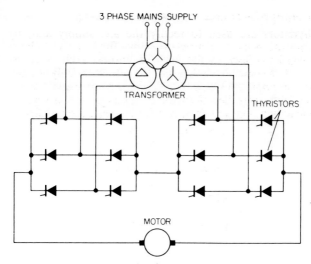

3 PHASE MAINS SUPPLY

TRANSFORMER

THYRISTORS

MOTOR

Fig. 85.—Three-phase 12-pulse thyristor bridge.

resistor required varies from two to 1 times the starting resistance as the machine speed falls from top speed to zero.

The plugging circuit is opened just before the motor comes to rest, either by means of a plugging switch, mounted on the motor shaft, that opens or closes its contacts in accordance with motor speed, or by means of current or voltage-operated relays incorporated in the control gear.

How is dynamic braking obtained ?

With a shunt motor, the field is left excited from the supply whilst loading resistors are connected across the armature which has been disconnected from the supply. The machine then acts as a loaded generator, presenting a braking torque that is proportional to armature current and field flux. This torque can be kept high by reducing

123

the loading resistance and therefore maintaining armature current as the speed falls.

With series-wound motors, either the armature or field connections must be reversed for braking after the motor has been disconnected from the mains. Braking continues so long as the machine is able to self-excite.

10

LINEAR MOTORS

What is a linear motor?

A linear motor can be thought of as an ordinary rotating machine that has been cut along one side and rolled out flat (Fig. 86). There are as many types of linear motor as there are rotary types, but the linear induction motor has found the most widespread application. The winding connected to the supply is known as the primary and the other one is called the secondary.

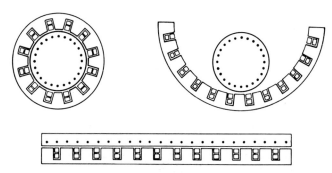

Fig. 86.—'Unrolling' a conventional rotary motor to produce a linear machine.

125

How does the linear induction motor work?

When the conventional induction motor is opened and rolled out flat the rotating field produced by the stator (the primary) becomes a linearly moving field and this induces a current in the rotor (now called the secondary). This reacts with the applied field from the primary and produces the torque of the motor as in the conventional rotating machine. But because of the new configuration, this torque now·produces linear motion. Clearly one winding must be considerably longer than the other or the two would simply separate when the current was switched on. There are therefore two types—the short primary and the short secondary.

How do short primary and short secondary linear motors compare?

The short primary type is normally found in applications where long distances are to be covered, as in transportation systems, where it would obviously be uneconomic to wind a long three-phase primary along the length of the track. The short secondary type is useful where only a short distance has to be covered and the secondary is very light. In both of these cases the secondary may consist simply of a flat conducting plate.

What are the main applications of linear motors?

There are many applications including pumping of liquid metals, opening doors, driving conveyor belts, but the two major applications are in driving overhead cranes and in propulsion of high speed trains.

How does the overhead crane linear motor work?

In this application the I beam that supports the crane functions as the secondary and a three-phase primary winding is attached to the frame of the motor which travels along the I beam on wheels (Fig. 87). This arrangement avoids all the complications associated with rotary motors—reduction gears drive shaft, etc.—with resulting simplification of maintenance and improvement in reliability.

126

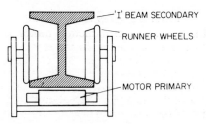

Fig. 87.—Linear motor arrangement for driving an overhead crane.

How is the linear motor used to propel high speed trains?

Although some trains are in operation using linear motors, the application to high speed transport is still in the development stage. One configuration that has been suggested is the double primary arrangement shown in Fig. 88. The power is picked up from the trackside by a brushless arrangement that works on the transformer principle. The train would be supported by an air cushion as in the hovercraft. An alternative system which would provide magnetic levitation as well as propulsion is currently being investigated.

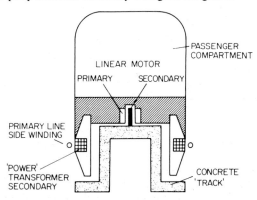

Fig. 88.—Section through a vehicle for high speed train propelled by a linear motor. The power is picked up by transformer action from the line side winding.

127

INDEX